STREETWISE DRUGWISE

For a complete list of Management Books 2000 titles,
visit our web-site at http://www.mb2000.com

STREETWISE DRUGWISE

Dr Eva Roman

and

Dr Richard James

2000

First published in 1998 by Management Books 2000 Ltd,
Cowcombe House,
Cowcombe Hill,
Chalford,
Gloucestershire GL6 8HP
Tel: 01285-760722. Fax: 01285-760708
e-mail: MB2000@compuserve.com

Printed and bound in Great Britain by Biddles Ltd., Guildford and King's Lynn

British Library Cataloguing in Publication Data is available

ISBN 1-85252-228-3

Acknowledgements

Our grateful thanks go to Lindsay Clive Smith for all his help and support; to Clive Insley of BAAS for supplying valuable information and organising two interviews; to Dr A M Ahmad and staff for their help and provision of interviewees; to ISDD for guiding us through valuable information; to PC Danny Beavan and PC Angela Lofts of the Youth and Community Section at Bexleyheath Police Station for their co-operation as well as allowing us to attend some school drug lectures; to Julian Dawton for providing the diagrams shown in this book; to the Health Promotion Unit, Beckenham Hospital for sharing information with us; and to the six participants who very kindly allowed us to write about their experiences of drug and alcohol use.

Contents

INTRODUCTION   11
   The most dangerous substance of all...

1. DRUGS   13
   Growing use in our society – availability of supply –
   options for using – challenging the habit – the case for
   openness

2. THE DRUG CULTURE   21
   Its attraction – running the risks – peer pressures – an easy
   escape – patterns of dependency

3. DRUGS IN SOCIETY   29
   Key drivers of use – group dynamics of drug use – a grow-
   ing dependence – the vulnerable individual – sources of
   supply and demand – dangers of the supply chain.

4. THE DRUGS   39
   Description – effects – signs & symptoms – remedies/
   treatment

   Alcohol   40
   Alkyl Nitrites (Poppers)   46
   Amphetamines   49

Anabolic Steroids   *53*
Barbiturates   *58*
Benzodiazepine Tranquillisers   *61*
Cannabis   *64*
Cocaine/Crack   *69*
Ecstasy   *73*
Gammahydroxybutyrate (GHB)   *78*
Hallucinogenic mushrooms   *81*
Heroin   *84*
LSD   *90*
Methadone   *95*
Opium   *98*
Over-the-counter drugs   *101*
Prescription-only medicines   *104*
Solvents and volatile substances   *106*

5. DRUG MIXES – 'Snidey Drugs'   111
   Bulk additives   *112*
   Mixes   *113*

6. DRUG SLANG   114
   Common names of street drugs   *115*
   Common names of drug mixes   *126*
   Slang expressions   *126*

7. SIGNS AND SYMPTOMS   133
   Physical symptoms (alphabetical order)   *134*
   Non-physical symptoms (Behavioural changes –
   personality changes – Social changes – Physical changes)   *137*

8. REMEDIES AND ASSISTANCE   142
   First Aid for Drug Users (listed by symptom, in alphabeti-
   cal order)

9. INTERVENTION   157
   Breaking free – lessening the harm

10.CASE STUDIES   164
  'Jules': recreational drug user   *165*
  'Mike': reformed alcoholic   *170*
  'Peter': chronic alcoholic   *173*
  'Russell': habitual misuser   *177*
  'Sandie': mixed drug misuser   *182*
  'Lindsay': ex-drug dependent   *186*

POSTSCRIPT: *What does the future hold?*   194

APPENDIX: *Useful contact numbers*   199

LIST OF DIAGRAMS
  i.   *Drugs: market penetration in England & Wales*   *15*
  ii.   *Percentage of those aged 16-29 who have taken drugs,*   *16*
        by drug taken.
  iii. *Categories of use*   *27*
  iv.   *Social, psychological & physiological aspects*   *34*
  v.   *Drug categories by effect*   *38*
  vi.   *Classes of Drugs (Misuse of Drugs Act, 1971)*   *110*
  vii. *Common symptoms of drug misuse*   *132*
  viii. *Factors determining drug misuse*   *160*
  ix.   *Harm minimalisation*   *163*

Introduction

The most dangerous substance of all...

Drugs are among the most emotive subjects in our society today. Confronting the problems of drug misuse raises moral questions which few people seem prepared to answer or even publicly debate. There is a deepening rift between those who abhor all forms of drug misuse and advocate only the severest penalties, and those who see the inconsistency of permitting some potentially dangerous substances for recreational purposes while banning others. Other people still feel it might be more useful and humane to help drug-addicted individuals, rather than automatically sending them to prison. The paradox, of course, is that the less society seems prepared to confront these problems, and the more 'authoritarian' the authorities become in response, the more people – almost half the population under thirty have now sampled illegal drugs – seem prepared to 'give it a go'...

The result has been an information vacuum, which this book hopefully goes some way to redress; as it is clear that, while very many people are prepared both to try and use illegal stimulants, they are doing so vicariously, often from a position of ignorance. Others, too, may find through ignorance that they are led into the way of dependence on drugs through perfectly innocent usage, for instance of prescription drugs, of whose effects they are unaware. The strictness of the law, and the climate of moral prohibition that has accompanied it, are, arguably, contributing to the dangers of drug misuse by keeping people in ignorance of the effects of drugs, both good and bad.

Taking this thought further: how, for instance, is a parent or teacher supposed to know if a young person has been taking drugs? How can they identify which of the many street drugs available may be being misused? What ought they to do about it – apart from march the miscreant down to the nearest police station, which is not always a helpful course of action, particularly in a medical emergency? And how can the individual – parent, teacher, carer, beat constable, first aider, elder brother or whoever – deal with just such an emergency, when someone's life may be at stake, if they are in complete ignorance of the cause of the problem and the likely outcome?

True, publishing information about drugs and their effects might possibly enable someone to sample a substance with more confidence; or to learn about a new, more interesting drug; or to mix a more potent cocktail, and could therefore be said to be 'aiding and abetting' drug misuse. But this kind of information and – more dangerously – mis-information is available on any street corner, take it or leave it. Having access to accurate and more complete information, however, could equally well stop someone from starting on a potentially dangerous course in the first place; while, in an emergency, it could help save lives.

For this reason, it is felt that publishing a lay person's guide to street drugs, their characteristics, symptoms, common names and effects, and methods of treating the medical emergencies they sometimes cause, is just one step towards a more open and honest debate that could have a very real value in helping individuals to make the right decisions in circumstances where lack of knowledge could be highly dangerous. For, the most dangerous 'substance' of all is ignorance... This book, then, is not an incentive for people to break the law; rather, it is a belated recognition that they are choosing to do so in greater numbers than ever; that they can be protected at least from some of the less desirable consequences of their actions – and may possibly, through having knowledge of the likely effects, be dissuaded from ever trying drugs in the first place.

1

The Danger of Drugs

Not all drugs are dangerous. Those used for medicinal purposes, either prescribed by a doctor or available without prescription, usually bring about beneficial results. Even some of the drugs which are open to abuse can have beneficial effects when administered under medical supervision, although the difficulty of conducting large-scale tests means that the jury is still out on controversial claims, such as the use of cannabis in relieving symptoms of nausea in patients undergoing chemotherapy.

Some drugs – and other, more sinister substances – are perfectly legal, yet also very dangerous when taken in excess: alcohol, for example; tobacco, which contains nicotine, one of the most poisonous and addictive substances known; benzene, a common additive in unleaded fuel; and solvents used in household products, which produce drug-like effects, yet whose long-term abuse can cause serious physiological harm.

Drugs may be taken in order to give the user a psychological or physical lift, giving them a strong feeling of wellbeing, lowering inhibitions, boosting energy and increasing stamina. Other drugs may calm the user down, helping them to sleep – or temporarily affect the way they perceive the world, providing vivid new experiences and opening

13

new vistas of the mind. But whatever drugs are taken for, there is a universal principle at work which broadly states that there is good and bad in everything, and that what goes up, must come down... Once people have experienced that easy, immediate switch in their psychological state, produced by whatever drug substance is adopted, the downward spiral of dependence will have commenced, and a habit may soon be established as a way of coping with the worst aspects of life. Unfortunately, some people never seem to imagine that these might include drug addiction! Reproducing this same 'fix' time after time may, in the long run, cost the user dearly in terms both of adverse physical and psychological reactions and an ever-increasing necessity to up the dose. As the 'highs' get higher, the 'lows' get correspondingly lower, requiring ever-larger doses for the user to get back 'up'.

Needless to say, the stronger the substance, the more costly the habit becomes. In a typical pattern of addiction, the habitual drug user becomes less economically active, the more he or she needs to earn in order to support their habit. They are then forced to look along increasingly illegal paths for the never-ending supply of money they need, thus being sucked further into a world of crime and personal degradation.

The trouble is, this cliché'd view of the morally depraved drug user resorting to crime is no longer, if it ever was wholly, true. Drug dependence often starts from the most innocent of experiences, or is linked purely to occasional social activity, when it is reasonably under control. It is difficult to 'demonise' people who use drugs in this way, although one can and should point out the very real risks attached, and the fact that it is against the law.

It seems that the stronger the drug, too, the more danger is attached to its use. The legal penalties become much more severe, for one. So why do people take drugs in the first place? There are probably as many answers as there are drug users. In some circles it appears the fashionable thing to do – one trial cannot do any harm, surely? while, to the bored and confused teenager, a certain element of danger and thumbing their nose at their 'elders and betters' may offer a challenge, a rite of passage into adult life.

People with cumulative personal problems may see the experience as a way to unload or even block some of these difficulties – for the time being at least. Others, lacking willpower, may succumb to pressure from their circle of friends to join the drug group, perhaps after some minor setback – an exam failure, or being stood up on a date. Many reasons exist why the 'drug slide' is climbed in the first place. Drug use does not pay any regard to class or social environment, all are affected. No patterns have really been established. Some individuals are clearly more at risk than others, but it is impossible at present to identify those likely to suffer possibly fatal adverse reactions, or to say who might be more susceptible to becoming addicted.

A recent report published by the Home Office Research and Statistics Directorate states that almost one in two young people – 45 per cent of those under 29 – admit to having tried a prohibited drug at some point in their lives. A breakdown of their findings is set out in Figures 1-2. Clearly, drug taking has broken through as a social phenomenon on a par with many other recreational pursuits, and we need to look for broader reasons than just individual weakness or criminality to explain it.

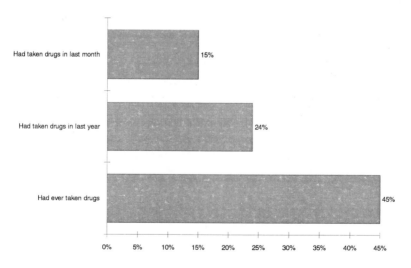

Figure 1. Percentage of those aged 16-29 who have taken drugs.
(Source: Home Office Research and Statistics Directorate: British Crime Survey 1996)

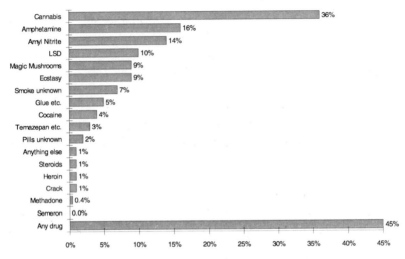

Figure 2. Percentage of those aged 16-29 who have taken drugs, by drug taken.

(Source: Home Office Research and Statistics Directorate)

Availability of supply

The supply of drugs is chaotic, and their availability varies from area to area. However, there is seldom any problem in finding them. Friends, family and neighbours may have or know of sources of supply, nightclubs and certain pubs are always fruitful ground, in some areas pushers are well-known – there is no difficulty in buying something, provided the payment is available. But, although the smuggling operations are clearly efficient, at street level the market is quite disorganised. Messages on the drug market grapevine soon spread to the right quarters and the goods appear from nowhere. Needless to say, once a chain of supply is started, local demand usually increases. What varies, however, is the actual drug on offer; the supply of, say, heroin or cannabis will often depend on the success of the authorities in intercepting shipments.

There are many different drugs on the illegal market and most of them are identified on the streets by colourful slang terminology, which we will go into, as best we can, later in Chapter 6. Those to whom the drug world is foreign territory will be bewildered by the range and variety of this slang language, particularly parents who suspect that their offspring are experimenting with drugs. It can be very frustrating when impenetrable slang is used to conceal the real drug terms, and a glossary such as ours may be helpful; having said that, new terms are being coined every day.

Street drugs come from a variety of sources, some are manufactured, grown or illegally acquired from legitimate sources in this country, while others are smuggled into the country by air and sea. The main overseas producer areas are South America, particularly Columbia, and South-East Asia – the so-called Golden Triangle on the borders of Laos, Cambodia and Thailand. Together with Turkey, Pakistan and Afghanistan, these are the main producers of opiates and cannabis, where whole regional economies may depend on growing poppies and pot for the global market. It has been a focus of international policing operations to destroy crops in these areas; but increasingly, economic measures are being used to try to wean farmers off drug crops as, otherwise, whole communities would starve.

But what about the dangers? These are considerably increased by the black market method of supply which, being underground, is answerable to no authority. Drug use is never 100 per cent safe, since there is no quality control or product regulation. Safety will depend on the type of person using it, where it is taken, the strength and purity of the drug and the length of time between each 'fix'. People tend to experiment with drug contents and often mix different substances together. Careless drug taking – either in large quantities or by shared injections – can lead to the passing on of infections (see next Chapter). Once this starts, it may well be too late to do anything positive to avert disaster.

Much of the supply chain depends on recruiting distributors who run most of the risks of being caught and imprisoned. These will tend to be drug users needing money to supply their own habit. Ultimately, what they supply to the end-user is of no concern, and later in the book we will look at some of the ways in which drugs are adulterated, often lethally, in order to increase profits.

Ultimately, the danger is that users are unable to stop. The deeper they get involved, the more dependency develops. Initial effects soon lessen and doses are increased. Before long, the user will look for more and more frequent intake which in turn will make the body scream for further fixes. Without their daily 'prop' the world in which the addict exists fails to provide safety and a feeling of being O.K. There may also be physical effects which are caused by the drug changing the body chemistry. So the dangers of the drug trade are considerable – and real.

Options for use

Drug use can mean different things to different groups of people. It could involve the use of any illegal street drugs or massive intake of drinks containing stimulants. Many drug users will, after initial trials, experiment with different drug mixes, always hoping to stumble across a potion which will increase the sensations already felt by the original drug fix. This experimentation can often produce adverse effects and people will go through 'bad trips'. The body may also develop tolerance to different drugs and will, in turn, need increased amounts to regain the initial effect. How much of an increase will depend on the after-effects and the level of drug dependency. Failing to meet this increased need can produce physical withdrawal symptoms which will then require further doses to counter the feelings of illness and unease.

The use of drugs can produce adverse physical reactions which may lead to the user becoming unconscious. If someone is found to be in trouble and the condition is suspected of being caused by drug reactions, it is important to be aware of what to do in an emergency. Drug overdoses can often be rescued through quick intervention and action in rendering first aid prior to more qualified assistance in a drug unit of a hospital. Later chapters (7 and 8) will help you to cross-refer the symptoms which may present in a medical emergency with the likely type of drug that may be involved, and the correct method of treatment.

Challenging the habit

But what about long-term help, to get an individual off drugs permanently? Society often judges the rights or wrongs of drug use in subjective terms and tends to be quick to condemn. People with drug problems may realise that they need help but are reluctant to seek advice through lack of knowledge about places which provide guidance, because of their criminal associations and past activities, or because they feel ashamed of their weakness. Or, the reluctance may simply be because they enjoy the habit and are just not ready to stop... Not all drug users lack willpower!

The drug user has stepped outside the bounds of civilised society: he or she knows it, and may feel a powerful sense of shame and guilt. Reassurance that people are on the user's side, are non-judgemental and have a genuine desire to help them back on the road to a drug-free life style should be the first consideration. Thereafter, with the co-operation of the drug user (who needs to provide answers to a number of relevant questions), assistance should be available to point the way forward.

Many possible forms of help and treatment from qualified people and organisations are there for the taking, some useful contact numbers are given in Chapter 9, but the first step on the road to recovery will have to be taken by the drug user themselves. Many of us may know someone who has already experimented with drugs, or who may be using them with increasing regularity, or who is well past the initial stages of dependence or addiction. This book is aimed at helping you to identify the danger signs, and to know what to do about them. This might apply to parents, older siblings, neighbours, friends and teachers, as well as to carers, counsellors and the emergency services.

The following chapters of this book, then, are intended to de-mystify drug use, and hopefully steer those who are contemplating drug experimentation into more healthy and danger-free habits. We have tried, as far as it is possible for authors of an 'older' generation not actually in the drug culture to do, to use current street terms that will have some meaning to users, and to define them hopefully to others. Chapter 6 ends with a glossary of street drug 'slang', which is offered with the proviso that terms and their meaning will change, almost from neighbourhood to neighbourhood and from day to day. 'Street', of course, is a slang expression itself, meaning the illegal market for drugs.

The case for openness

This is not to say the authors approve of drug taking: far from it. We would never recommend anybody to start out on a potentially harmful process which they may not be able to stop. However, we have argued that there is a case for more openness about this problem, as drug takers are no longer a hidden minority in our society. Knowing more about the drug culture, including its colourful terminology, is vital to understanding the problem. As we have seen, nearly half the population under thirty claim to have sampled illegal drugs at some time (and a far higher proportion regularly use legal drugs like alcohol and cigarettes). Worryingly, quite a large number of these self-identified users admit to having taken drug substances without even knowing what they were... It is surely only right therefore, that people should have access to the information they need to make life-choices in their own best interest, and to be aware at least of the potential consequences for their health and continuing liberty.

2

The Drug Culture

Experimentation with street drugs is carried on nowadays by a great many people from all walks of life. The drug scene knows no social barriers, and people use drugs for a wide variety of reasons; some to obtain pleasure, and some to relieve pain (both may be equally illusory). Today's drug scene can be split into two distinct cultures, although we make no moral distinction. These are classified as the 'recreational culture' and the 'habitual culture'.

The recreational culture tends to use illegal drugs with discrimination, and not usually full-time. On the face of it, members appear to be in reasonable control of their habit. Users will mix freely with groups who have similar habits, and statistically come to little harm. The 'I can take it or leave it' attitude is, to a large extent, correct; the drug taken in moderation is not normally 'dangerous', and these groups derive a certain amount of pleasure from its recreational use, from the shedding of inhibitions it encourages, and from joining in group activities where the experience is in some way enhanced by it.

However, peeking beneath the surface, there may well be more deep-seated reasons why people get sucked into these groups, and become influenced by those who encourage them to join. The individual who is perhaps more than ready to become part of this environment is often susceptible to social pressures. He or she may feel that to opt out would mean being excluded from social or recreational acceptance by people they like and look up to, which in turn would isolate them and cause feelings of becoming a social outcast. Often, there is a 'leader' – a strong individual who stands to benefit, financially or psychologically, from recruiting new members of the group, and who may have a foot in both drug cultures. The user defers to the power and quasi-parental authority of this individual. Once the user defects from the recreational culture, they may be more easily compelled by such individuals to join the alternative, habitual culture – where the rules are very different.

Running the risks

Despite the efforts of police and Governments worldwide, illicit sales of virtually every banned substance known to affect people's moods and perceptions have increased rapidly in recent years, while in some neighbourhoods entire communities are being brought down by the increase in drug abuse and related crime. It's a massive problem worldwide – though the latest Home Office surveys do show that, among young people in some areas of the UK at least, the increase in drug misuse may have stabilised in recent years.

Why do so many people run the risk of misusing potentially lethal substances? It will largely depend on what types of drugs are being used and the reactions derived from each substance. Mood changes can take place, giving the user a 'lift'. The amount of energy people put into activities such as sports, or dancing, and their ability to sustain effort over a long period, can be artificially enhanced. Some drugs will aid relaxation, or assist with sleeplessness, or decrease physical or emotional pain. Some drugs are used to counter the effects of other drugs. Conversely, feelings of great achievement, heightened creativity (usually false) and wellbeing can be obtained. Other drugs will have the effect of lowering inhibitions changing people's personal 'image', the way other people see them – or the way themselves perceive the world around them, stimulating new insights into the nature of reality. Whatever the reason, we should remember that people have been abusing substances in this way in every society for many thousands of years. It seems to be just 'something we do'!

Peer pressure

Users are also starting at a progressively younger age. Despite consistent attempts to provide information and education in schools and colleges, drug habits formed by older pupils are still being passed on to those younger ones who are initially doubtful about 'trying out' some of the drugs on offer, but who find it hard to resist peer pressure. Availability seems to be no great problem; as even the Home Secretary found to his cost, there is always someone who knows of a source where a drug may be obtained.

One of the principal attractions of early drug use is 'joining in'. No young person wants to feel excluded, to be in a minority of one. If pressure is put upon the individual, it becomes much more difficult to refuse at least to try out what the others are already using. Naturally, if the sensation turns out to be pleasurable, young people soon develop a need or craving for further sensation which allows them to forget the pressures for a while. Adolescents are often worried, both in the immediate present over exams for instance, their developing 'self-image', their personal relationships – and for the future. It is terrible, not knowing what life holds in store, but suspecting the worst... and not feeling you can trust anyone else with your problems. If the young person can find some ready means which allows them to forget their woes, they will resort to artificially induced feelings of well-being more and more frequently until eventual dependence sets in.

An easy escape

Turning to drink or drugs is often an easy escape route when a person has experienced a major setback, such as failing to get a university place, losing a job or breaking up with a partner. They may understandably feel that all the excitement has gone out of their life, and seek new ways of bringing back the sparkle. Loneliness is a terrible problem, too, in our 'winner-take-all society, obsessed as it appears to be with images of perfection and success. Naturally, if relief is obtained regularly within the circle of a reassuring group of fellow users, even though they are in no sense real friends, the person will come to believe that this is a perfectly normal way to gain acceptance, and to turn on that feeling of wellbeing whenever it is needed, even if 'society' doesn't approve.

In fact, people with personality disorders often seem more vulnerable to the pressures of the drug scene than most. They appear too weak to resist the temptation and quickly get drawn in, particularly if they find that the rest of the group accepts them more readily. More on this later.

Doing the business

Drug taking is also surprisingly rife within the business community. One of the main reasons why business people especially find drug taking attractive is that it makes them feel more confident, more able to achieve tough targets; and, above all, counters the stress and pressures created by the fast-moving, competitive environment. If you can impress the boss that your sales performance is red-hot and your 'leadership skills' are worth a bonus, then why not get a little help by artificial means? When this can be achieved by taking easily concealed substances which are not immediately identifiable – as opposed to hiding the vodka bottle in your desk drawer – no-one will guess that your business ability is artificially drug-enhanced. Certain professions are particularly prone to drink-and-drug dependence, partly because they provide precisely the kind of peer-group reinforcement and the 'conspiracy of silence' that dependents rely on, and partly because they attract risk-taking personalities that are pre-addicted to high-pressure 'thrills and spills'. Nemesis eventually arrives with executive burnout.

People often turn to drugs, either for social reasons or because there is a visible underlying problem. The housewife's constant feelings of depression may result in the doctor prescribing drugs over a lengthy period of time, until a psychological dependency is formed. Almost any chemical substance taken by whatever method, i.e., by mouth, through inhalation or by injecting will, when absorbed into the body, in some way produce effects, both physical and psychological – short-lasting and long, good and bad. If these effects are felt to correlate with a temporary happiness, then adverse effects, such as the far more unpleasant feelings of not having a supply of drugs to take, are ignored. Many users may not even be aware that they have a problem until it overwhelms them; while others turn to self-medication to encourage the problems to disappear. The more serious or deep rooted the problem, the more attractive the idea of shedding it – even if for only a short time – becomes.

However, the process is generally self-defeating. By taking drugs to alleviate the problem, rather than tackling the cause of the problem itself, the user rapidly finds themselves in a downward spiral. The 'cure' becomes the 'disease', leading to adverse legal, social and health situations requiring extensive counselling and medical support; the problem being that the addicted personality invariably refuses to admit that drugs are a problem to them (see Denial) and seldom seeks help, or succeeds in finding it, until they have literally been through hell.

Another route by which people may turn to drugs is after they have been involved in or witnessed some traumatic incident. This could include violence, even murder – robbery, rape, a car accident, or any other abnormal incident which would cause emotional as well as physical trauma. Such incidents typically produce a variety of reactions from irritability to mood swings, sleeplessness and lethargy, as well as physical symptoms such as breathlessness, palpitations, indigestion and the rest. The person may experience nightmares, or otherwise vividly re-live in their mind the horrors of the original event. They may suppress their memories and subsequent reactions, appearing depressed, forgetful and lethargic. To counter these obsessive patterns, the person turns to drugs – on which they subsequently become dependent.

Since some of these reactions, which incidentally are quite normal, may prevent the individual from carrying out necessary everyday tasks, drugs, often starting with alcohol, may be thought to be an easy answer; they help to mask or even temporarily eliminate the post-traumatic reactions, providing a short-term 'lift' or calming the individual sufficiently for them to be able to carry on with their daily work. However, prolonged drug use at prescribed dosages will in no way maintain the required results, and the user may attempt to get further relief, either by increasing the drug dose or by trying 'something stronger'. This method can easily encourage drug dependency as well as pushing the person into a deeper state of post-traumatic stress with subsequent, longer-lasting debilities. The outcome may be lengthy treatment, both for the initial traumatic experience and then for the drug addiction on top.

The slippery slope

How does this process happen? In two ways: psychological dependence, and physical addiction.

The majority of people who try out drugs, often quite legally or under prescription, experience positive feelings at first; often, over quite a long period of time. However, the body eventually learns to tolerate the dosage, and as the drug reaction begins to fade, the person may once again experience the old adverse feelings. This in turn creates a further craving to get back to the positive high felt on originally taking the drug. Although increasing the drug dose may well induce a new euphoric state, the body simply adapts again – leading eventually to psychological dependence, regulated entirely by the drug dosage.

Any artificially induced feeling of wellbeing can only help in short bursts; at best, it can help people get over difficult or stressful situations while natural healing, counselling or psychotherapy takes place – at worst, it will induce the patient to resort to the drugs more and more frequently, and thereby enter rapidly into a downward spiral of dependence. With some drugs, however, chemical changes in the brain lead to a more sinister condition which we can describe as 'addiction', where the habit of using the drug is quite beyond the control of the individual, and the penalties for withdrawal are severe.

CATEGORIES OF USE

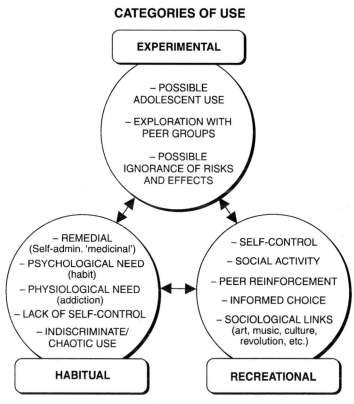

Figure 3.

Patterns of dependency

Drug use tends to be influenced by much more than just the actual drug substances being taken. The user's personal characteristics, their psychological make-up and past experiences, their strengths and weaknesses, all have a part to play in defining the addictive personality.

Lack of experience in drug use can often bring about additional dangers, where users are unsure about procedures and dosages, or unaware of possible side effects. Body reactions also play a large part in determining future patterns of usage: where one person will experience pleasurable reactions first time out, another will suffer horrific after-effects. A third person may in fact have little or no response to the drug and develop no further interest in it.

The social setting also plays an important part. We are all familiar with the 'rave culture', for instance. Here, in weekend-long dance marathons, 'uppers' are taken in order to produce the high energy level and stamina the raver needs. These will be followed by 'downers' in order to bring the user down to an acceptable coping level. Frequency of upper and downer use will eventually necessitate an increase in dosage and, to obtain the same required effect, the journey to more powerful substances will have started which can develop into dependency and, ultimately, addiction.

Two further possible factors leading to increased drug use, 'reward dependence' and 'harm avoidance', are the processes by which a person who is physically dependent on a particular drug will receive instant relief from withdrawal symptoms with further drug administration, which is then looked upon as a reward. As with all pleasurable, rewarding experiences, the user seeks to repeat the experience more often. In doing so, as a separate but welcome effect, the drug user will also continue to avoid the agonising experience of the abstinence syndrome, or 'withdrawal' – hence the harm avoidance aspect of continued drug dependence. This cycle oscillates from reward to harm, and back again, with increasing magnitude as the dose required to achieve either effect increases. Other problems, including physical addiction and the dangers of polluted drugs or overdose, then come into play, placing the individual at risk.

3

Drugs In Society

To some extent the 'sixties, and then the late 'eighties, saw the arrival of a new group of users who went through stages of experimenting with 'soft' drugs and hallucinogenics – ecstasy, LSD and cannabis, mostly at weekends. These users did not identify as drug addicts – they appeared to be young, 'straight' professional people for whom alcohol was not enough, who perhaps deplored the effects of drunkenness and sought something more sophisticated, who enjoyed the occasional use of drugs with their friends but were able to control the habit. One could classify this group as traditional social users who did not seek help from available sources since they enjoyed the habit and felt no need to ask for intervention.

What was not realised was that this group was actually 'addicted' to the *social aspect* of drug taking, and that this social aspect is, in fact a major stepping stone towards drug addiction. Flirtation, if you could call it that, with the more exciting aspects of the hard drug culture, particularly in America, as revealed through 'existentialist' films and music, provided the group with an ideal self-image that required borrowing all the cultural icons of reckless independence and self-destruction that bored young people so easily get attached to. The Thatcher years were a breeding ground for young people romantically – though often, with good economic reason – attached to the idea of social exclusion and affected with feelings of rootlessness and fragmentation. Exchange of local gossip relating to sources of supplies, local meeting places and other information of interest to drug groups; and – once people progressed to night clubs, festivals and 'raves' – exposure to stronger drug availability and connections with pushers, led them further into the habitual drug culture we looked at earlier, with drastic consequences for the weaker and more foolhardy individuals, and for long-term players. They were – are – literally playing with fire.

Group dynamics of drug use

Individuals or groups who misuse drugs tend to do so for a whole variety of different reasons, some of which will be informed, others compulsive. Peering beneath the surface, drug misuse does seem to begin frequently with social, psychological and physical characteristics common to adolescents and young adults. Research shows that this age group links into the drug scene through its disregard for traditional values. Drug dependence can develop out of rebelliousness, lack of social expectations, non-acceptance of social structures, frustration with an inability to express incoherent feelings; and, through circumstances, subscribing to minor criminal behaviour such as car theft or shoplifting. It's all part of a pattern of deviant conduct which could begin with truancy from school, underage smoking and drinking, withdrawal from family life, sexual promiscuity and, eventually, drug use as a means of showing independence, 'growing-up', or even hostility to authority. Such a pattern can also be a reaction to childhood neglect or abuse.

Young people may see drug taking as a step towards mature sophistication and adult behaviour which will gain them peer acceptance and approval. One in three people under 16 start smoking cigarettes for this very reason. The tragic paradox is that so many young people feel the need to reject the values of an older generation, only to end up creating identically flawed social structures of their own!

Curiosity is clearly another key factor which leads the young person towards drug use. The desire to explore areas which may provide new, thrilling, pleasurable and even dangerous experiences can become a very strong motivation and lead young people into the experimental stages of drug use.

Two factors, therefore, rebelliousness and curiosity, are relatively common in the adolescent and must account for quite a high degree of drug misuse within this group. If drug experimentation leads to being welcomed into a peer group, it is likely to persist, particularly if drug use produces ease and relaxation or avoids, temporarily, immediate problems. In this case there is every chance that the drug use will continue. Experimental drug misuse is usually – though not always – carried out within a group, with someone more knowledge-able on hand to supervise the experimentation and, hopefully, to point the uninitiated in the right direction regarding the safest use of illicit drugs. The experimenter will be without previous knowledge about the effects of the drug and their experience may not confirm the sensations they were led to expect, in which case they may be sufficiently discouraged from carrying on. If, however, their curiosity produces positive results, this can lead to acceptance within the peer group, where mutually supportive drug misuse is very likely to continue. If the substance produces pleasant feelings of ease and relaxation – eliminating, if only temporarily, problems which the individual has been unable to resolve – then there is every likelihood that the use of drugs will persist.

Once the experimentation stage has been satisfied and the group has made an informed choice about the particular drugs they intend to favour, the new user will enter into the recreational or social drug culture. Music tends to be the common denominator, as it exerts a very powerful influence on young people to conform, and to enter into the social culture through clubbing, where physical proximity and the use of designer drugs and alcohol help to break down barriers. Within this environment, ecstasy may well be one of the group's chosen drugs. (Heroin, by contrast, produces calm and mellow feelings, thus preventing the group from carrying on continual dancing all night.)

Users will also have thought carefully about the possible side effects of any particular drug. Within the recreational group, the use of drugs tends to be controlled. The decision to take the substance has been made, the quantity which will be taken at any one time is group-determined, the likely effects have been anticipated. There is also a feeling that there is 'safety in numbers', that if anything does go wrong, the user will readily find help. Recreational users are people who do not necessarily need to make use of drugs; taking drugs is, to them, a 'lifestyle choice', one that will raise the level of enjoyment of whatever else it is they are experiencing at the time. It is a world away from sharing needles in filthy toilets. However, this particular lifestyle may indeed produce social, emotional or relationship problems. For, although drugs by themselves rarely cause these, they may indirectly help to contribute to them, precisely because of the enhanced level of experience they promote – both good and bad.

A growing dependence

Dependent or habitual misuse of drugs is characterised either by a physical, psychological or social need. With physical dependence, the user adapts to a particular drug, developing a tolerance which is then followed by a withdrawal or abstinence syndrome. Tolerance requires that the original quantity taken needs to be increased progressively in order to achieve the same effect experienced by a smaller dose. The withdrawal syndrome will present physical changes when the drug is discontinued.

Psychological drug dependence embraces strong feelings of pleasure and satisfaction, but also produces the need to keep taking the drug in order to avoid the discomfort of intense craving if the drug is not readily available. This can lead to a marked change in lifestyle which often forces the addict into a chaotic phase. Since psychological dependence demands that the user must satisfy their craving – particularly if the preferred substance is unavailable – the individual will take anything they can get hold of, in order to satisfy their dependent need. They are no longer in control of their habit.

Research has shown that physical and psychological dependence can result, either from the use of the drug itself, or from the effects the user experiences. Certain drugs undoubtedly produce a physical habituation, whereas others will encourage a psychological dependence. For example, people may feel compelled to take a drug in order to get the psychological 'lift', but they also need it to avoid the physical 'down' that follows from not taking it.

Physical dependency on some drugs develops through repeated heavy use. This particularly applies to drugs such as alcohol, tranquillisers or heroin, the use of which is again steadily increasing. Following prolonged use, body chemistry is changed. When the drug is not available, unpleasant physical withdrawal symptoms will present if the substance is not repeated. Psychological factors may also come into play through continued, habitual use; some symptoms experienced during withdrawal tend to be conditioned responses which are established during previous withdrawal experiences.

The vulnerable individual

A considerable number of users who frequent street drugs appear to possess some personality vulnerability which was present prior to getting into the drug scene. Their coping mechanism for dealing adequately with the challenges of day-to-day life is underdeveloped, consequently they tend to be critical of authority and society. Many drug users also experience bouts of anxiety and/or depression. Others may have personality disorders or mental illness in the family or even come from quite distressingly disorganised backgrounds where often a history of childhood abuse or bereavement is common. However, many who misuse drugs do not display any of these characteristics, so it is hard to generalise.

It is frequently found that drug misuse is more prominent in societies which condone drug taking, where peer group pressures are often applied in order to give acceptance and status to the drug user. This can particularly apply to the socially dysfunctional person who will purposely increase his/her drug dosage and become the 'leader' of the group in which drug taking plays an important role. The individual's personality plays an important part in drug dependence.

Mental or physical trauma can encourage someone to become socially addicted to a support peer group which, in turn can lead to drug dependence. Psychologically induced drug need leads the individual into a false sense of wellbeing which will strongly force them to continue with the misuse so as to maintain the positive feeling of being O.K.

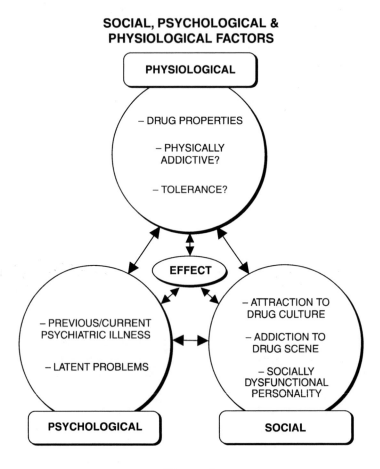

**SOCIAL, PSYCHOLOGICAL &
PHYSIOLOGICAL FACTORS**

Figure 4.

Sources of supply and demand

The myth that street drugs are mainly obtained from the various drug dealers who can be found in any large city centre is exaggerated.

The sale of illegal drugs has become a multi-billion pound enterprise which is usually headed by extremely rich people. Drugs are mainly brought into the country from other countries and are smuggled into the United Kingdom, usually in large quantities. These drugs consist, in the main of pure substances and are financed by very wealthy dealers who lay out vast amounts of money in order to sell the drugs on for distribution to the users.

The main objective is to sell the products to as many pushers as possible in order to realise maximum profits. This is always the prime aim and it is of no interest to the dealer how and in what form the user gets their particular 'fix'.

The development for large-scale marketing of drugs took place in the mid-'eighties. At that time, heroin was the accepted predominant drug culture with stereotyped users in the 35+ age bracket – mainly white males who were frequently unemployed and turned to minor crime in order to supplement their habit.

Drugs at that time had developed a very bad name and educational programmes were in the forefront warning against shared needle use and inevitable death. The year of the World Cup saw cannabis topping alcohol amongst younger people; users in the 35+ bracket favouring alcohol, whereas the lower age group of between 25-35 preferred cannabis.

The need for a more concerted effort in the marketing of drugs, particularly in the densely populated city areas, gave rise to the subliminal approach – if it is made acceptable, it will be used. The two most likely areas for targeting were found to be in fashion and music. Black bomber jackets with recognisably coded emblems emblazoned on the front or back provided the market with advertising facilities. Music outlets such as clubs were found to contain ready buyers for drugs like ecstasy, which became the emblem of the 'rave' culture. Young people were able with the aid of this substance to carry on dancing well beyond the normal level of energy through the 'lift' the drug provided. Ecstasy is thought to be a relatively safe drug, but a number of deaths have been reported due to adulteration with poisonous additives, and dehydration – while a very few people seem to be abnormally hypersensitive to the drug.

Due to its immense popularity among young people in their teens and twenties, and a firm belief in the harmlessness of recreational 'soft' drug use, the 'rave' scene has managed to break down any social barriers which may have inhibited the use of drugs. Ecstasy is clearly one of the key 'drivers' of the drug culture in Britain, and the worry is that there will continue to be crossover from recreational to habitual use of harder drugs, in addition to possible long-term psychological and physical effects which we are only just becoming aware of.

Dangers of the supply chain

Before any street drug gets to its final source, it will pass through the hands of between ten and fifteen dealers. This can be compared with the growth of a tree with its main stem (the top man) and the various branches (the pushers). Each one will want to make their own profit, therefore the drug will be broken down and mixed with any number of other substances in order to increase bulk. By the time the user buys the drug, it will contain no more than ten to fifteen per cent of the pure drug. Unfortunately, there is never any guarantee that the drug bought contains the substance promised. The only way purity can be established is by expensive analysis in a laboratory. This is usually carried out by the police or in a hospital.

Another problem of supply is the introduction of infective agents at various stages of processing, before the drug reaches the street. It's unpleasant to contemplate, but as the pure drug passes down the line of the various pushers, who may have turned their garages into drug factories, hygiene and disinfectants are very rarely used. The substance may have been stored in condoms or rubber glove fingers and swallowed by drug smugglers (mules). Once the 'package' (bullet), re-appears via the anus, cleanliness is of secondary importance and contaminants can infect the user who is totally unaware of the methods used to produce the mixture.

Research has shown, however, that fewer than ten per cent of the younger generation obtain their drugs directly from 'dealers'. In the main, drugs are passed on by brothers or sisters, anyone else in the family or through a circle of friends. If people try to experiment with drugs and find the outcome favourable, they may try to influence others to try as well. There is, however no guarantee that the next person will have an equally enjoyable experience; drugs affect people in different ways and one man's pleasure will be another man's poison. So the flow of drugs is seldom direct.

Money is always of prime importance where drugs are concerned and one way to buy is for a group of people to pool their resources and appoint one person with the right contacts to buy for the group. Personal contact with dealers or pushers tends to be kept to a minimum and mobile telephones have largely taken over the task of establishing contact with other dealers or those wishing to purchase.

A variety of inconspicuous locations and illegal sales venues may consist of vehicles such as furniture removal vans, repair vans, minicabs – even ice cream vans and milk floats have been identified as drug selling points.

Drug dealers will usually avoid selling to younger people, simply because they are not likely to have the ready cash available and, of course, there is always the risk that they will identify the person who sold them the drug, particularly if the effect was adverse. Should youngsters come into contact with dealers, they will most likely be at the bottom end of the branches and may well be small-scale local pushers who are users themselves.

A further source of obtaining drugs is from the elderly who may be selling their own prescription drugs in order to supplement their low incomes. This practice can, of course lead to senior citizens depriving themselves of vital medication whilst feeding someone else's cravings. The transaction can also lead the pensioner into being blackmailed into providing further supplies which, if detected, will bring about heavy fines or even prison sentences. Although the cost of drugs has reduced, once the habit becomes established, more money will be required and this often leads to the downward trail. An established drug dependency will often cost between £70 and £100 per day. Users

DRUG CATEGORIES BY EFFECT

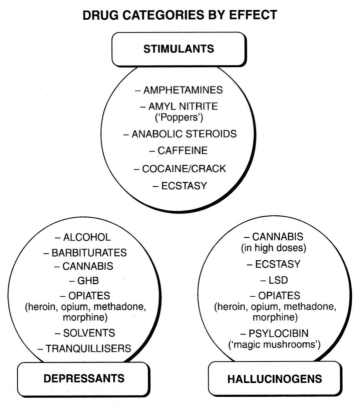

NB: Some drugs may fall into more than one category. Note also that many substances will act as hallucinogens when taken in sufficiently high doses.

Figure 5.

have been known to steal in order to satisfy their cravings and, if all else fails, then the user may even turn to prostitution. It is not until the individual has really hit rock bottom and realises that they may lose everything – husband/wife, children, home and means of support – that they will hopefully come to their senses and seek help from reliable sources.

4

The Drugs

Set out in the following pages is a listing of the most commonly available street drugs, their history, characteristic effects, side-effects and methods of treatment in emergencies. Although the list may not be exhaustive, it includes all the main types of illegal drug available on the streets at the time of going to press.

ALCOHOL
(Booze, Drink, Liquor, Bev)

Description

Ethyl Alcohol or Ethanol is a volatile liquid which is obtained through the action of yeast mixed with sugar or glucose. This mixture is fermented with fruits, vegetables or grains such as hops, rice, etc. to give flavour, and then diluted with water to the required strength.

Spirits, which include rum from molasses, whisky from malted grain, gin from grain and juniper berries and brandy from wine are fermented and then distilled. In their raw state they contain an oily substance which consists of Amyl and Butyl Alcohols. These have a more injurious effect on the nervous system than Ethyl Alcohol.

Alcohol is a depressant drug which slows down the nervous system, dulling the body's functions and the thinking reactions. The liquid when entering the body is very quickly and completely absorbed.

Physical characteristics apply to a small amount (about one fifth of any dose taken) being absorbed in the stomach while the rest is ingested in the upper part of the small intestines within two to three hours of drinking.

The body can receive one fifth of the total energy it needs from alcohol intake, as alcohol preserves carbohydrates and fats taken in food. This will produce a tendency to store these substances in the tissues as superfluous fat when alcohol intake increases greatly without reduction of other foods. Hence the tendency for heavy drinkers to gain weight.

The mental effect of increased alcohol intake often depends partly on its effect on the circulation and also on its anaesthetic reaction on the nervous system. This will dull pain, worry and anxiety. A similar dulling action on the greater intellect can lessen self-criticism and self-control which then creates the false impression that the alcohol is producing a stimulating effect. Alcohol is not a stimulant, but a depressant. Before long, as the dose is increased, movement and behaviour become dulled and deteriorate, resulting in slurred speech and poor coordination – which in turn can interfere with decision making and delay actions, hence the dangers of drinking and driving. In more advanced stages of alcoholism, the sense of perception and skilled movement deteriorate, and eventually stupor or heavy sleep set in, lasting until all the alcohol absorbed by the nervous system has been oxidised and consumed. Finally, on awaking, the drinker may notice the characteristic hangover effect: headache, nausea, dry mouth, disorientation and an aversion to noise and bright lights.

Heavy alcohol intake will produce severe sleep disturbance (apnoeia) which can lead to broken sleep which is of a poor quality and anything from two to six hours duration. The higher the intake, the more likelihood of heavy withdrawal symptoms on waking will show in addicts. Once the first drink of the day has been taken, it will produce vomiting after which the alcoholic will return to bingeing until sleep or stupor overtakes them.

In acute stages of alcoholism, people may drink excessive quantities of the substance over a short period (bingeing). But alcoholics can train themselves to survive on very little alcohol, and even remain 'dry' for long periods – while for some unlucky souls, just one drink may produce all the characteristic signs of a full-blown binge. Ordinary drunkenness produces, in the first instance, bright, witty behaviour, loquaciousness and a general feeling of wellbeing. As the inebriation develops, however, the mood swings become more extreme; a phase of excitement/depression becomes recognisable when people can become angry, resentful, melancholic, tuneful or violent, grow maudlin and may even produce weeping fits – or all of these in turn.

As the alcoholism becomes more pronounced, there will be a distinct downward spiral during which all feelings of shame are lost with dulling sense of power. The person will be reeling, with blurred vision, slurred speech, lack of co-ordination, loss of balance, nausea, vomiting, leading to possible panic attacks, unconsciousness and coma.

The most striking/dangerous symptom to be considered is that which can occur amongst people who have drunk heavily and persistently for several years and who then attempt to reduce or stop using alcohol. The condition in question is Delirium Tremens, often known as Blue Devils, or D.Ts. This may occur shortly after cessation of drinking (approximately 1-10 days) and presents as a medical emergency. Delirium Tremens is a state accompanied by hallucinations. The first signs of the onset will often be tremors felt all over the body, especially in the hands and tongue. This will be followed by complete loss of appetite, sickness, vomiting, diarrhoea and temperature rise, a weak rapid pulse and constant purposeless movement. Finally, hallucinations occur during which the person sees horrific images such as spiders, giant flies, mice or rats, snakes, etc. Sometimes,the alcoholic will confuse people with figures of authority such as police personnel or even masked hangmen. This may be followed by the ultimate stage of a terrified or raging type of delirium during which the alcoholic could be in danger of committing suicide or even homicide. If the body has become weakened and dehydrated, physical illness such as pneumonia may set in which produces a considerable risk of mortality if this condition fails to be recognised and treated. Chronic alcoholism can affect the mental state of the person, who then passes on to a condition of mental feebleness due to organic changes in the brain. The last two stages represent medical emergencies and will require hospitalisation with constant supervision and careful nursing.

Despite this, approximately 60 per cent of alcoholics will go back to drinking after treatment and get worse. There is at present a high relapse rate, probably partly due to a general increase in social stress as well as a much younger generation of drinkers. For another 30 per cent, however, treatment holds out the prospect of a permanent cure.

Chronic alcoholism is a disease, to which drinkers may be at least in part genetically disposed. There is, however a difference between the chronic alcoholic and the excessive drinker. The latter will be able to control the habit and even stop drinking if the reason for terminating is sufficiently reasonable. The former cannot make the effort to abstain for more than short periods. It was pointed out by an expert who claimed: *"The regular heavy drinker lives to drink but the alcoholic must drink to live".*

However, excessive drinking is not to be encouraged, especially in the young, as there is no way of knowing beforehand, whether one is a heavy drinker or an alcoholic. It is certain only that alcoholism never develops in people who don't touch drink.

Effects

The substance in alcohol consists of a depressant drug which slows down the user's reaction and brain functions.

Excessive drinking affects the body's co-ordination and results in slurred speech. The more a person drinks, the more adverse symptoms develop – which can include double vision, nausea and eventual loss of consciousness with disturbed heavy sleep, followed by an unpleasant hangover.

Psychologically, alcohol effect will depend on the state of the user's mind as well as the situation in which the drink is consumed. The condition will undoubtedly deteriorate if the person is suffering from depression.

As is well known, alcohol can affect people adversely by making them violent. The drink can lower inhibitions which often makes people behave recklessly.

If someone becomes unconscious while under the influence of alcohol, they may vomit; and, since muscle control is no longer functioning, they may inhale their vomitus and choke.

Fatal overdoses have occurred when alcohol is mixed with 'downer' drugs like heroin or tranquillisers – or, more innocently, with barbiturate sleeping pills or even paracetamol.

Drink in moderation may be slightly beneficial. People who are habitual drinkers for long periods can develop diseases of the heart, stomach, liver and brain. Alcohol has a cumulative effect which, if taken in excess will lead to a physical dependence. The tolerance level will require constantly increased doses in order to obtain the same stimulation.

Signs and symptoms of alcohol misuse

- Odour on the breath.
  Alcohol may disguise the concomitant presence of other drugs.

- Intoxication.
  Make sure that no outside physical harm comes to person.

- Difficulty focusing, glazed appearance of the eyes.
  No action needed, condition will eventually improve.

- Uncharacteristically passive behaviour or combative and argumentative behaviour.
  Remember one cannot offer any help if one allows oneself to come to any harm.

- Gradual (or sudden in adolescents) deterioration in personal appearance and hygiene.
  Use tact.

- Gradual deterioration of function, especially in job performance or school work.
  Use tact, suggest help is available.

- Absenteeism (particularly on Monday).
  Investigate other possible reasons.

- Unexplained bruises and accidents.
  Investigate other possible reasons.

- Irritability or personality change.
  Offer help or suggest counselling.

- Flushed skin.
  Investigate other possible reasons.

- Loss of memory or blackouts.
  Consult medical opinion.

- Availability and consumption of alcohol becomes the focus of social or professional activities.
  Point this out.

- Changes in peer-group associations and friendships.
  Find out why.

- Impaired interpersonal relationships (troubled marriage, unexplainable termination of deep relationships, alienation from close family members).
  Offer support and counselling.

- Loss of consciousness
  Dial 999, check breathing and pulse. CPR if necessary.

- Delirium Tremens (D.T.'s)
  Seek medical advice.

Remedies/Treatment

In the event of unconsciousness, the most appropriate course of action will be to put the person into the recovery position. This will provide intrinsic safety and enable the situation to be monitored. It will also prevent choking if the user vomits.

Talking to the person will help to prevent them from slipping further into possible unconsciousness. Putting people into a bed and 'letting them sleep it off' will only add to the dangers of becoming more deeply unconscious, go into a coma and even die.

Drinks of water, if the person is only drowsy, should be given very sparingly, with small sips at a time. Coffee should be avoided since this is a stimulant and the person then absorbs the alcohol faster. Fresh air may help.

In extreme cases an ambulance should be called, as excess alcohol content in the stomach will have to be pumped out by experts.

ALKYL NITRITES
(Poppers, Snappers, Bananas, Rush)

Description

Amyl nitrite, butyl nitrite and isobutyl nitrite are the most misused members of this group of volatile liquids which have a rather sweet, fragrant odour when fresh – and the tell-tale smell of old socks when the odour has been around for longer periods! Amyl nitrite was first used to relieve angina (chest pain due to cramp in the muscles of the heart) in 1859, but its use has been superseded by more specific medications.

The term 'popper' is derived from the sound that one of the more popular containers makes when opened – a glass capsule – the cap of which needs to be popped off to release the vapours from the gold-coloured liquid within. Frequently, nitrites are sold in small, screw-top containers, holding approximately 10ml of liquid.

The characteristic rush or flush with dizziness and light headedness has made alkyl nitrite use popular with the dance drug culture and with younger users. The fumes from the nitrites are absorbed quickly through the mucus membranes of the lungs into the bloodstream. Unfortunately, nitrites have an effect on haemoglobin – the chemical in the blood which carries oxygen around to the tissues – whereby it changes its chemical formula, reducing its effectiveness in carrying oxygen to all the tissues. The general tone of the arteries is reduced and, because of this, the user will feel very faint if they get up from a prone position too quickly; the blood is settled in the lower parts of the body and does not go up to the brain.

Medical preparations containing alkyl nitrites are readily available and are currently purchased through mail order, sex shops, joke shops and gay bars. They are often sold as air fresheners and, as such, have no legal controls. Poppers are not classed as illegal drugs, but can nevertheless produce dangerous side effects, especially when taken in combination.

Effects

When the vapours are inhaled, they cause relaxation of the muscles in the walls of the small arteries. These arteries widen and blood flow through them increases. This produces a characteristic rush or high when the blood vessels to the head and brain are dilated, although nitrites do not act directly on the nervous system. The effect starts within a few seconds of inhalation and lasts just a few minutes, necessitating frequent repeats.

If repeatedly taken, however, poppers produce a severe headache as well as nausea. The heart rate increases, other smooth muscles are relaxed, notably those of the anal sphincter (this is why nitrites are popular amongst the gay community, since the drug eases anal intercourse). There is no real evidence that they may help to enhance or prolong orgasm.

Tolerance does occur after about three weeks' continuous use of nitrites but sensitivity is restored after a suitable period of abstinence. There is no evidence of physical or psychological dependence from use.

Nitrites can cause tell-tale soreness of the skin around the nose and mouth and also within the nasal passages. If spilt directly upon the skin, a sore rash develops.

Another reaction likely to take place is a feeling of 'time standing still'. There is a reduction of blood pressure which will impair the sense of balance and often induces fainting, particularly if increased physical exercise has taken place. The heart tries to compensate by beating faster. People who suffer from raised blood pressure are more at risk when taking poppers. This drug also increases eyeball pressure, which can lead to blindness, especially for anyone suffering from glaucoma.

If the drug is swallowed in large quantities, this can lead to the user becoming unconscious and, in fact, some deaths have been reported.

Signs and symptoms of Alkyl Nitrite misuse

• Headache.
  It will pass.

- Fainting.
  Check pulse, breathing. Be prepared to resuscitate. Lie person down out of harm's way. Loosen clothing.

- Dizziness.
  May precede fainting.

- Flushed face and neck.
  Exclude other causes such as heat-stroke or infections.

- Unpleasant odour (old socks).
  The odour worsens as nitrites age.

- Nausea.
  Be aware vomiting might follow.

- Facial rash.
  Seek medical advice if persists.

- Collapse /coma if high intake.
  Dial 999. Check pulse and breathing. CPR may be needed.

- Raised pressure inside eyeball (glaucoma).
  Seek medical advice.

- Red, painful eyes with poor vision.
  Seek medical advice.

- Breathlessness in long term frequent users.
  Seek medical advice.

Remedies/Treatment

The user may immediately become breathless and dizzy, with possible fainting. The recovery position should be used, which will also prevent vomitus being inhaled if the person vomits.

With high, repetitive intake of this drug, the person may well slip into a coma which requires fast removal to hospital by ambulance.

AMPHETAMINES
(Speed, Whiz, Sulphate, 'Phets)

Description

Amphetamines are a group of synthetic drugs which act as stimulants on the central nervous system in much the same way as adrenaline, so that users are wide awake and 'raring to go'.

Tolerance develops with amphetamine. The more a person takes, the more they need to take in order to obtain the same effect. Although physical dependence itself does not seem to be a problem, there is a strong psychological dependence as the user seeks to find that sense of wellbeing that is induced by the drug, or to recapture the initial rush. Taking more averts the feelings of fatigue, hunger and depression experienced when amphetamines are stopped. Once the drug 'high' has worn off, the user will feel fatigued and depressed and needs more of the drug in order to avoid the unpleasant after-effects.

Amphetamines were first synthesised in the late nineteenth century in search of drugs for the treatment of depression. Nowadays they may be used legally for treating a rare disorder of marked sleepiness (narcolepsy) or when treating attention deficit disorders in children.

Amphetamines were used widely during the Second World War for soldiers, workers and housewives left alone at home, to keep them going. In the 'sixties, the 'mods' favoured amphetamines to stay awake in all-night clubs. A group of older, intravenous users appeared at the same time, having switched from heroin and cocaine which had just been banned. 'Amphs' are favoured particularly by young people involved in the dance culture, who might also be using other drugs such as LSD and ecstasy. They are also valued by young women watching their weight because of their appetite suppressant effect.

Most of the amphetamine on the streets is amphetamine sulphate which can be in tablet, capsule or powder form. The powder is usually sold in 1 gram wraps. Street purity of amphetamine is usually no more than 5 per cent. It is customarily consumed orally, by injection or sniffing. It is often dissolved in soft or alcoholic drinks, or the powder may

be dabbed on a wet finger and sucked in much the same way as sher-
bet. In the late 'eighties a new, smokable form of one of the amphetamines, methylamphetamine, made an appearance on the street market. Known as ice, meth-crystal or ice-cream, a clear glassy rock or
crystalline material is smoked using a small, round pipe.

The drug is used in three different ways:

a)   sniffing
b)   swallowing
c)   injecting

of which the third method is the most risky.

Amphetamine is an illegal Class B drug (although, if prepared for
injection, it is counted as Class A) which again carries with it a high
fine and long prison sentence.

Effects

When taken, amphetamine acts as a stimulant, producing a feeling of
increased energy, power, confidence, a reduced need for sleep and a
marked reduction in hunger. Many people feel anxious and edgy.
There is an increase in heart rate, respiration rate, rise in blood pressure, dilation of the pupils and dryness of mouth. Higher doses cause
flushing, sweating, headache, teeth grinding. Sadly, when the effect of
the drug wears off, the user is left feeling tired, irritable, depressed
and unable to concentrate.

Especially after regular use, there are feelings of confusion, psychosis with paranoia (amphetamine psychosis) and sometimes violent
behaviour. The psychotic effects may be more pronounced in those
with latent mental illness.

Often, especially if injected, amphetamine is used on a run lasting
several days and when used this way, induces delusions and hallucinations. Acts of aggression are more likely to occur.

Heavy or long term use gives rise to problems with the heart and
circulation. Sniffing amphetamines can cause damage to the lining of

the nose. Injecting carries the risk of infection at the injection sites with HIV and hepatitis being common.

Since the drug is an appetite depressant, the user may experience weight loss which will cause them to feel run down. This can leave the body open to all kinds of infections, while anorexia in women gives rise to malnutrition and cessation of menstruation.

Continued use of amphetamines can trigger off underlying psychiatric problems and also encourage psychosis, at which point a user may suffer from hallucinations, i.e., being followed, watched or persecuted. Amphetamine psychosis in which paranoia is a predominant feature is fortunately reversible once the amphetamines are stopped.

Amphetamines can encourage very strong cravings for the drug which in turn can eventually cause epileptic seizures and death.

Signs and symptoms of Amphetamine misuse

- Dilated pupils (when large amounts are taken).
  This will wear off. Move to darkened room may help.

- Dry mouth and nose, bad breath, frequent lip licking.
  Moisten lips with water.

- Excessive activity, difficulty sitting still, lack of interest in food or sleep.
  Try to prevent dangerous incidents. Encourage food and drink intake.

- Irritable, argumentative, nervous.
  Reassure.

- Talkative, but conversation often lacks continuity; changes subject rapidly.
  Patiently listen.

- Runny nose, cold or chronic sinus/nasal problems, nose bleeds.
  Seek medical advice.

- Paranoia (irrational fear of persecution)
  Seek medical/psychological intervention.

- Psychosis (uncontrollable or violent behaviour)
  Seek medical/psychological intervention.

Remedies/Treatment

Since this drug produces excessive energy which is 'borrowed', the user may become overheated, which can lead to dehydration. This will require water and salts such as non-alcoholic sports drinks to replace the body fluid.

Panic attacks will require calming the person down. Reassurance will play a large part in this situation, making it clear to the person that this tense, panicky feeling will wear off gradually.

The person would benefit from being moved to an isolated quiet area away from loud noises or very bright lights. Should the user start to overbreathe (hyperventilate) then this often very fast breathing and gasping for breath will produce dizziness and possible nausea. A paper bag (not plastic) may be placed over the mouth and nose so that exhaled carbon dioxide is re-introduced into the lungs.

Should the condition worsen, medical aid must be sought.

ANABOLIC STEROIDS
(Dianabol, Anavar, Sustanon, Stanozolol)

Description

Anabolic Steroids are a group of hormones responsible for the building up of body tissues. A prime example of a naturally occurring anabolic steroid is testosterone. Testosterone has both androgenic and anabolic effects. The androgenic component is responsible for the male sex hormone effects. Thus, as well as controlling the development and function of the male sex organs, it is responsible for the development of male secondary characteristics such as increased body hair and deepening of voice. Testosterone also has anabolic properties. These cause development and growth of muscle tissue. Research has, in the past, failed to produce a synthetic steroid hormone which has only anabolic effects without some androgenic stimulation as well. This is because most synthetic anabolic steroids are derivatives of testosterone.

Anabolic steroids have a very limited legitimate medical use. They may be used to treat rare anaemias, cancers and some rare hormonal conditions. Their use for reasons other than these is much frowned upon. The muscle building effects of anabolic steroids are frequently misused in gymnasia and health clubs by athletes and by those in competitive body building who wish to increase their muscle bulk for cosmetic reasons. In the rave scene, men wanting to impress when they strip off as they overheat will want to improve the look of their torso by building it up with anabolic steroids. Anabolic steroids are also used by those involved in occupations requiring overt strength. Thus bodyguards and bouncers might welcome their use.

Most of the steroids sold in the United Kingdom are produced in underground laboratories, many as fakes of the original products. Often, when purchasing these steroids, as with many other street drugs, the dose will be unreliable and may be adulterated with other impurities. Users often take them in combination with a whole range of body building products such as high protein powders. Frequently steroids are injected as well as being taken orally, sometimes known as 'stacking'. They are frequently taken in a cycle with a period of use followed by a period of abstinence. The effects that the user is looking for are obvious; there is clear increase of muscle bulk, though this might not necessarily be of increased strength. However, the side effects can be horrendous (see Effects below).

Anabolic steroids are not truly addictive, although some research does indicate that frequent users do exhibit many of the markers for psychological dependence. Irritability and depression occur when the dose is reduced. If the dose is continued, then the typically enhanced masculine psychological traits are maintained.

Anabolic steroids are controlled under the Misuse of Drugs Act as a Class C drug, making unauthorised supply an offence. However, it is not illegal to possess them. Anabolic steroids are only available on prescription. It is not illegal to possess the drug for personal use but it does become illegal if it is passed on or sold to others. There appears to be a very large illicit market in anabolic steroids which is constantly growing, despite the mandatory drug testing and other measures now carried out by many organisations. As the financial rewards for winning and the cost of training increase, anabolic steroids will continue to be used by those who feel it necessary to cheat at sports.

Effects

Anabolic Steroids increase muscle bulk and hence strength and energy. However, there is a distortion of the normal control of the body's internal environment, and the drugs produce a great number of adverse side effects, including baldness, acne and raised blood pressure, with concomitant raised heart rate. There may also be insomnia, water retention, mood swings and aggression. Long-term side effects include damage to the liver and kidneys (including jaundice, tumours and cysts), heart disease and strokes.

The body's defence mechanisms to fight infection are suppressed, as are the normal responses to major illnesses. The person using anabolic steroids will not develop a fever to warn them of an infection. Neither will they respond in the same way to pain.

If the drug is used by young people, it may produce stunted growth if they are still in the process of growing. Male users may develop infertility with symptoms of testicular shrinkage and a tendency towards breast growth.

Females may develop the opposite symptoms such as growth of body hair, the voice deepening and possibly clitoral enlargement. Some of these changes and side effects in women may not be reversible.

Recent research has shown that steroids in some cases can cause addiction and withdrawal symptoms may be experienced when users stop taking the drug. Professional help will then be necessary to counteract the withdrawal symptoms.

Signs and symptoms of Anabolic Steroid misuse

- Increased aggression, mood swings.
  Avoid confrontational situations.

- Increased body hair.
  May be permanent.

- Deepening of voice.
  May be permanent.

- Abscesses in injected muscles.
  Seek medical advice.

- Recurrent infections.
  Seek medical advice.

- Acne.
  Seek medical advice.

- Increased muscle bulk.
  Not always healthy muscle.

- Cessation of menstruation.
  Will return when drug taking ceases.

- Male infertility.
  Will probably return.

- Water retention – puffy face and lower legs.
  Seek medical advice.

- Jaundice.
  Seek medical advice.

- Stunted growth in teenagers.
  Irreversible.

- Delusions of grandeur.
  Award OBE...

- Psychological dependence.
  May require counselling.

- Hallucination.
  Reassure, avoid harmful situations.

- Stroke.
  Hospitalise.

- Heart disease.
  Seek medical advice.

Remedies/Treatment

Users of this drug may suffer from hallucinations and aggressive phases. Calming the person down and reassuring them during these episodes should be attempted, provided there is no risk of violence.

There is a tendency for frequent anabolic steroid users to suffer a stroke or heart disease. This requires quick removal to hospital, so an ambulance must be called, The person should be placed on the floor in a semi-prone position, leaning towards the affected side in the case of stroke evidence, and their condition must be monitored. Should breathing stop, cardio-pulmonary resuscitation should commence.

BARBITURATES
(Downers, Barbs, Sleepers, Goofballs)

Description

Barbitone, a synthetic derivative of a known sleep inducer, urethane, was first introduced to the therapeutic world in 1903. Since then, many more derivatives have been manufactured. All the barbiturates are depressants of the central nervous system. Different barbiturates are used to quieten (sedatives or tranquillisers), induce sleep (hypnotics), as short-lasting anaesthetics or to prevent epilepsy. Most come in powder form – made into tablets or in capsules. Some are in injectable liquids within glass ampoules. The barbiturate group of medicines was popularly prescribed by the medical profession in the 'fifties and 'sixties as tranquillisers and sleeping medicines, and became a favourite method of committing suicide. However, their addictive properties and danger in overdose very quickly saw their decline in use in favour of the newer benzodiazepines group of tranquillisers and hypnotics. One of the barbiturates, phenobarbitone, is still commonly prescribed to prevent epileptic seizures.

Today, tighter controls on barbiturates, the widespread availability of benzodiazepines and the rise in heroin use mean that barbiturate misuse is a negligible part of the illicit drug scene. Users of other drugs, especially opiate dependants, may turn to barbiturates to ward off withdrawal symptoms if they are unable to obtain their usual supplies. Barbiturates may also be taken to help people calm down after taking amphetamines or LSD.

Barbiturates are a Class B drug. Maximum sentence for possession is five years' imprisonment and a fine. A fourteen year imprisonment and a fine may be imposed for supplying barbiturates.

Supply is usually stolen – either from medical outlets such as pharmacies or from homes where they are prescribed medicines. There are a variety of different types, amongst which are: Amytal, Nembutal, Seconal, Soneryl and Tuinal.

Effects

Barbiturates depress the central nervous system in a similar way to alcohol and when taken orally, their effect depends very much on the quantity taken. A small dose (one or two pills) makes people feel relaxed, although the person may be clumsy and have slurred speech. As the dose taken increases, there may be mental confusion followed by sleep and coma. Overdose (sometimes with just ten pills) can cause death because respiration stops. All the effects are potentiated when barbiturates are mixed with alcohol.

Intravenous users dissolve the powder in water before injecting and the sought-after effects (and risks of overdose) are almost immediate. Barbiturates are perhaps one of the most dangerous drugs to inject since the injection is extremely irritant and gangrene can easily occur if an artery is used.

Psychological and physical dependence easily develops with regular use. Tolerance occurs so that the user needs more and more barbiturate to induce the same desired effects. However, the corresponding amount needed to cause respiratory failure increases very little so that the risk of death from overdose increases. The margin between the dose needed to produce the desired effect and the lethal dose is small.

Withdrawal symptoms after regular use include irritability, nervousness, inability to sleep, nausea, hallucinations similar to those of alcohol withdrawal, and even convulsions. Withdrawal effects subside within about a week.

Signs and symptoms of Barbiturate misuse

- Symptoms of alcohol intoxication with no alcohol odour on breath.
  Alcohol is often dangerously mixed with barbiturates.

- Lack of facial expression or animation.
  This wears off.

- Flat emotions.
  Characteristic of depressant drugs.

- Unkempt appearance.
  Person no longer looking after themselves.

- Slurred speech.
  Should improve as drug wears off.

- Sleep
  Recovery position is safest to avoid inhaling vomit.

- Cessation of respiration
  Dial 999. Check pulse and start resuscitation.

Remedies/Treatment

Since this drug is a strong sedative which slows down the operation of the central nervous system, there is a very high risk of overdosing which can prove fatal. If the person shows signs of slurred speech, loss of co-ordination and is slipping into unconsciousness, he/she should be placed into the recovery position and carefully monitored in case breathing and pulse stops. CPR must then be carried out, having first dialled 999.

BENZODIAZEPINE TRANQUILLISERS
(Benzos, Moggies (Mogadon), Jellies, Tranx)

Description

The benzodiazepine tranquillisers (so called minor tranquillisers) were introduced in the 1960s as a safe alternative to those drugs already being used by doctors to treat anxiety. The benzodiazepine family of drugs include chlordiazepoxide (Librium), diazepam (Valium), lorazepam (Ativan), temazepam (Normison) and nitrazepam (Mogadon). Some (notably temazepam and nitrazepam) were marketed as a hypnotic, though any benzodiazepine given in high enough dose can induce sleep .

In the late 1960s and 1970s, the benzodiazepine tranquillisers were often prescribed for long-term use to those patients with anxiety disorders and even those with normal stress responses. Prescription for use as a hypnotic was popular. Today, they are used more to provide temporary symptomatic relief while longer-term solutions to problems of anxiety and stress are put in place. They are also prescribed as effective muscle relaxants to treat, for example, muscle spasm associated with injuries or cerebral palsy. Diazepam can be used to stop an epileptic fit in progress.

Street use of benzodiazepines became clearly apparent in the mid-'eighties. Users were easily able to inject temazepam drawn directly from capsules which was the main prescribed preparation of temazepam at the time. It became their choice of drug when heroin was in short supply, or if they could not afford heroin. Those not injecting take benzodiazepine orally to 'come down' from stimulants, to augment the effects of alcohol – or just to feel relaxed. There is no illicit manufacture of benzodiazepine – enough can be stolen or procured from legal sources. Supplies are generally derived from Temazepam obtained legally on prescription, or from thefts from pharmacies and wholesalers. People under the care of their doctor may well exaggerate their need for prescribed benzodiazepines in order to sell the excess on the street.

Hoping that they could prevent misuse by injection, the manufacturers of temazepam changed the formulation inside the capsules from liquid to a gel. But users simply warmed the contents of these 'jellies' until liquified and then injected. Unfortunately, once in the veins, the gel solidified again and caused obstruction in the vein. Today only tablet forms of temazepam are produced – users crush these, dissolve the powder and inject.

Benzodiazepine is controlled under Class C of the Misuse of Drugs Act.

Effects

The main effects of benzodiazepines are to lessen anxiety, relax muscles and induce sleep. Because of these effects, they do, to some extent, reduce inhibitions.

Drowsiness and reduction of manual dexterity, slowing of thought processes and memory are all side effects. Very large doses which can only be reached rapidly enough by injection can stop respiration. This very rarely occurs. Injecting does run the risk of infection at the injection site with further risk of septicaemia. Needle sharing further widens the risk to include HIV and hepatitis.

Long-term regular use of benzodiazepine presents a problem with withdrawal. The withdrawal syndrome includes feelings of intense anxiety and panic, lack of sleep, palpitations, sweating, tremor, muscle fatigue and loss of appetite. The onset of symptoms may sometimes be delayed for up to ten days following cessation of use and may last several weeks. Some reports suggest that withdrawal symptoms may occur if regular use had been for as little as four weeks.

Signs and symptoms of Benzodiazepine misuse

- Symptoms of alcohol intoxication with no alcohol odour on breath. *Benzodiazepines are frequently used with alcohol.*

• Slow, confused, poor memory.
  No action needed.

• Slurred speech.
  General coordination also may be affected. Avoid driving and using machinery.

• Sleep
  Recovery position is safest to avoid inhaling vomit.

• Scars or needle tracks if injection used
  These can be infected. There is a risk of Hepatitis and HIV if needle sharing.

Remedies/Treatment

Since this drug is a strong sedative which slows down the operation of the central nervous system, there is a very high risk of overdosing which can prove fatal. If the person shows signs of slurred speech, loss of co-ordination and is slipping into unconsciousness, he/she should be placed into the recovery position and carefully monitored in case breathing and pulse stops. CPR must then be carried out, having first dialled 999.

CANNABIS
(Dope, Puff, Blow, Weed)

Description

Cannabis was first introduced into Western medicine in the mid-19th century from China, where it had been used both as a herbal remedy and for recreational purposes since ancient times. In Britain, recreational use of cannabis was prohibited in 1928 but it was not until 1973 that the Misuse of Drugs Act prohibited the medical use of cannabis. Recreational use and self-medication with cannabis remain an integral part of West Indian culture; indeed, 'ganja' has a sacramental status in the Rastafarian religion.

Cannabis comes from the Cannabis Sativa plant. This grows best in hot countries but is easily cultivated in Britain. (A recent spate of thefts of large floodlighting systems betrayed some impatience on the part of growers with our shorter winter days...)

The active ingredients in cannabis are the tetrahydrocannabinols (THC). The main forms of cannabis are used to provide the user with this ingredient.

Herbal cannabis from the leaves and stem (grass, dope, ganja, marijuana) looks like dry tobacco.

Cannabis resin (hashish, hash) is a resin scraped or rubbed from the plant, compressed into browny/black blocks (like oxo cubes).

Cannabis is normally smoked mixed with tobacco in a hand rolled cigarette (joint or spliff). Special pipes may also be used. Cannabis resin has to be crumbled first before mixing. Commonly, a regular smoker may smoke one or two joints several times a week. Resin is also put into drinks, or baked in food (happy birthday cake).

Effects

The effects of cannabis vary according to its strength (often horse manure or herbs are mixed with cannabis to increase the bulk) and the

64

quantity smoked. The situation, mood, mental and physical health of the user all go to vary the effects. Cannabis is often used by heroin addicts if heroin is in short supply. The effects generally start a few minutes after smoking and may last between one and three hours, depending on the dose. When eaten or drunk, it takes an hour or more to work but may last twelve hours or longer.

The cannabis user hopes the drug will cause mild relaxation, loosen up inhibitions, free creativity and induce feelings of wellbeing and euphoria. The user may become talkative, laugh or giggle when in a group, but some people when 'relaxed' by cannabis become intro- spective and reflective. Not all forms of cannabis produce the same result though, and some users are disappointed to feel no effect at all. Larger doses make people forgetful, impair manual dexterity and ren- der them unable to think properly – hence the increased number of accidents that occur to cannabis users. It is therefore advisable to avoid driving while under the influence, and indeed, anyone testing positive to cannabis whilst driving may be prosecuted.

Sometimes, cannabis may cause severe distress and confusion, or feelings of panic and paranoia (suspicion of other people). High doses, for example from a strong batch or from certain stronger forms of cannabis such as sensimilia (a strong herbal form), may cause effects not dissimilar to those experienced if LSD is taken. Hallucinations and confusion may become more intense, leading to very distressing panic attacks, especially if the user is already anxious or depressed. This is why cannabis is included in both the depressant and hallucinogenic categories of drugs in the diagram entitled Drug Categories by Effect, set out on page 38.

Cannabis causes an increased heart rate, lowering of blood pres- sure, nausea and vomiting, bloodshot eyes and dry mouth. It has been reported that regular male users suffer a reduction of sperm count with resultant infertility. Babies born to mothers who are heavy cannabis users are not only low birth weight and sickly because of the effects of tobacco smoke itself, but are more at risk suffering with neonatal tremor, distress and irritability as a result of the cannabis.

It would be wrong to assume that there are no harmful effects from taking cannabis. It is true that there is no overwhelming evidence that

THC itself is dangerous. But this may, in the main, be because few scientific tests or studies have been carried out to conclusion and most users do not advertise the fact. There have been reports that physical dependence is possible. Psychological dependency is very likely and regular users find it hard to stop. When smoked, there are collateral dangers from mixing it with tobacco – users become addicted to the nicotine, and suffer the usual side-effects of smoking.

It has foolishly been said that cannabis is good for asthma sufferers because THC itself causes opening up of airways in the lungs. No asthmatic with any sense will report that the smoke and tar from a joint helps their breathing! The strong, sweet, sickly smelling smoke, which is rich in tar, is more harmful to the lungs than tobacco smoke and therefore carries all the same health risks as smoking ordinary cigarettes – bronchitis, emphysema, arterio-sclerosis, cancer of the throat, lung and bladder, and so on.

Tests have shown that the drug can be detected in the urine for anything up to thirty days, which will enable testing to go on for much longer periods. If the drug is detected – since it is classed as an illegal substance – or the user is found to have it in their possession, the maximum sentence at present is five years and there is also an unlimited fine imposed. Supplying the drug carries a much longer prison sentence, up to 14 years. Joint passing or sharing also carries a heavy fine, since it is perceived as supplying.

There is, however, a strong movement for the decriminalisation of possession of small amounts for personal use. The courts differ widely in their sentencing policy according to where you are in the country. In practice, most first offenders now are merely cautioned by the police, although it is stressed that a caution remains on your record and may be taken into account when sentence is passed for a subsequent offence. It will also render you liable to suspicion in the future, and could have an impact on employment prospects. Even a small sentence can have large repercussions!

Signs and symptoms of Cannabis misuse

- Rapid, loud talking and bursts of laughter in early stages of intoxication. Sleepy or stuporous in the later stages.
  Ensure person doesn't lapse into unconsciousness or coma.

- Forgetfulness in conversation.
  Nothing to do but be patient.

- Hallucinations in high doses
  Reassure if frightened. Protect from any physical harm.

- Inflammation in whites of eyes; pupils unlikely to be dilated.
  This is caused by the smoke.

- Sweet, sickly smell, sometimes reminiscent of certain types of aftershave popular in the 1960's.
  Open window.

- Burn marks on clothing where hot, loosely packed herbal cannabis has dropped out of cigarette.
  Point out the dangers of this.

- Distorted sense of time passage – tendency to overestimate time intervals.
  Point this out.

- Use or possession of paraphernalia including 'roach' (filter paper) clip, packs of rolling papers, pipes or 'bongs'.
  It is not illegal to possess these items.

Remedies/Treatment

Should the person show signs of anxiety, depression or paranoia, reassurance should be provided. If confused, users should simply be steered gently in the direction of a chair or sofa (cannabis users are docile and easily persuaded). In case of fainting, loosen clothing, keep warm and place in the recovery position. If fainting persists, call an ambulance.

COCAINE/CRACK
(Coke, Charlie, 'C', Snow, Rocks, Crack)

Description

Cocaine is derived from the leaves of the coca bush and has stimulant effects similar to those of amphetamines. Four and a half thousand years ago the South American Indians chewed coca leaves for their stimulant properties. Coca tonics and medicinal brews containing cocaine were popular in the nineteenth century when cocaine, the active drug within coca leaves, was first extracted in its 'pure' form. For many years, cocaine was successfully used as a local anaesthetic for eye and dental surgery. However, the professional medical and dental world never really made use of the short-acting stimulant properties of this white powder, which occur when it enters the central nervous system or brain via the blood stream. Amphetamines are more easily absorbed and their effects last longer.

Laws restricting the sale and use of cocaine came into effect in the early years of the 20th century and today, cocaine and all its various salts are controlled under Class A of the Misuse of Drugs Act.

From an expensive recreational drug of the 'sixties and 'seventies, cocaine became a high fashion drug of the 1980s amongst people in the media and entertainment business and those in the fast-moving financial centres of the world.

Traditionally, cocaine hydrochloride powder would be chopped up into fine lines on a hard surface like a mirror, using a razor blade, and then snorted up into the nose through a straw. Users soon learnt that the cocaine hydrochloride could be converted to a smokable cocaine 'freebase' crystalline preparation – 'crack' – and that the effects of the cocaine could peak much quicker if smoked, because the smoke passes easily through the vessels lining the nose and lungs into the blood stream. Dealers soon had ready-made crack to sell on the street.

Crack – small, irregularly shaped, off-white pellets about the size of raisins – thus started to appear as a form of cocaine which would easily release its powerful vapour if heated either in a cocaine kit or in one of the many home made 'pipes' made from tin cans or bottles with glass or metal tubing which enable easy heating and smoking of cocaine. The tiny rocks make a cracking noise when heated, hence the name. Crack became notorious due to lurid stories of 'crack heads', addicts prepared to use extreme violence to obtain enough money to feed their habit.

Typical recreational users of cocaine might sniff 1/4 gram over a weekend. A more regular user may consume up to 2 grams. Once again, the law is very stringent and mere possession of the drug will lead to many years' imprisonment or heavy fines.

Effects

When smoked (or 'freebased'), the euphoric effect of crack cocaine is felt almost immediately, peaks in a couple of minutes and wears off within 15 minutes or so. Sniffing takes perhaps 30 minutes for the effects, which are not so intense, to peak.

A cocaine 'hit' induces a rush of excitement and exhilaration, feelings of wellbeing and greater mental capacity, even though, in reality, there is no such improvement. Whilst experiencing these feelings, the user may be more talkative and cheerful though sometimes anxiety, panic, paranoia and even hallucinations may result, especially if large doses or a 'spree' of repeated doses over a period of hours is taken.

Physical effects include a dry mouth, dilated pupils, sweating, loss of appetite, increase in heart rate, buzzing in the ears, wheezing and diarrhoea. The local anaesthetic effect of sniffed cocaine causes burning sensations in the nose and, as the drug wears off, a runny, inflamed and sore nose occurs.

When the cocaine effect wears off there is a comedown with tiredness and even depression. Although physical tolerance does not develop with cocaine nor any physical withdrawal symptoms, further hits of cocaine are needed to make the depression go away. The euphoric feelings experienced when taking cocaine make it easy to develop psychological dependence for those who can afford to. Long-term regular users will suffer restlessness and weight loss (because

70

they have no other appetite). Paranoia and anxiety are particularly obvious long term side effects.

Overdose of cocaine is rare but it does occur. It is the heart that suffers because of the rapid pulse rate that results. The heart is unable to beat fast for too long and starts to skip beats, quiver and stop. A heart attack often follows which can prove fatal. Injecting cocaine can lead to thrombosis, infection and, if sharing needles, HIV and hepatitis.

Sniffing cocaine is less dangerous than smoking it since the sensation develops gradually and lasts longer, but it can damage the nose lining. Smoking crack is more harmful, being very quick-acting and productive of very forceful reactions. It can also cause lung damage.

Worse still, as with other injectable drugs, a cocaine dose will reach the brain very rapidly. This can have adverse effects such as seizure or overdose. Impurities can cause septicaemia and other infections. Frequent injections will damage veins, which can eventually collapse. They can also lead to thrombosis and abscess formation.

Both cocaine and crack 'hits' tend to be very short-lived, which encourages the user to increase the dose in order to obtain the same result. The higher the dose becomes, the more likelihood there is of overdosing, in whatever form. If the drug is taken on a continuing basis, the user may well develop hallucinations which can lead to paranoia and psychosis. A compulsion to keep taking the drug will establish itself.

'Speedballing' – injecting a cocaine and heroin mix – appears to have a high death rate.

Signs and symptoms of Cocaine & Crack misuse

- Dilated pupils (when large amounts are taken).
  This will wear off. A move to a darkened room may help.

- Dry mouth and nose, bad breath, frequent lip licking.
  Frequent sips of non-alcoholic drinks.

- Excessive activity, difficulty sitting still, lack of interest in food or sleep.
  Avoid dangerous incidents. Encourage food and drink intake.

71

- Irritable, argumentative, nervous.
  Calm, reassure. Avoid confrontation.

- Talkative, but conversation often lacks continuity; changes subject rapidly.
  Patiently listen.

- Runny nose, cold or chronic sinus/nasal problems, nose bleeds.
  Seek medical advice.

- Injection site abscesses, septicaemia
  There is a risk of hepatitis and HIV if needle sharing. Medical help needed.

- Use or possession of paraphernalia including small spoons, mirror, tin foil, metal straws, razor blades.

Remedies/Treatment

This drug will produce alertness, physical strength and false confidence. However, with frequent use it may cause breathing problems or possibly chest pains.

The person should be placed in a semi-prone position so as to lessen any breathing difficulties and help to ease any chest pains. If the condition fails to improve, an ambulance should be called.

In the event of the person refusing to go to hospital, advice to see the GP must be given. Reassurance is also important since the user may well be in an anxious state.

ECSTASY (MDMA)
('E', Doves, Apples, Pill)

Description

The chemical description for this drug is MDMA, its full title being 3,4 Methylenedioximethylamphetamine. Most users take this drug in tablet form but it can on rare occasions be sniffed, smoked or injected.

MDMA was discovered in the first decade of this century, when a large drug company was searching for a new pharmaceutical preparation based upon chemical manipulation of the amphetamine molecule. Other, related drugs were found to include MDA ('love drug'), MDEA ('Eve'), MDMA and MBDB. Some of these substances occur naturally in plants such as crocus, parsley, saffron, nutmeg and dill, but MDMA itself is entirely synthetic. They are all in the family of so-called psychodisleptic, or hallucinogenic, amphetamines; and, within the family, there is a spectrum of effects ranging from stimulant-only to highly hallucinogenic drugs, depending on their chemical structure.

Neither MDMA or its sister compounds were ever deemed safe or specific enough to be marketed. Any clinical use for this family of drugs, apart from amphetamine itself, was in the main discarded; although, in later years, MDMA was included in a list to be considered for use as an experimental agent in chemical warfare, presumably to extract information from prisoners. When MDA – the 'love drug' – was banned under US law in 1970, some 'therapists' started using MDMA to dissipate hostility and anger in their clients, as at that time it remained a legal alternative. In 1977 the drug was correctly deemed a Class A controlled drug under the Misuse of Drugs Act, 1971. Illegal and often very unreliable synthesis of the drug continues to satisfy the increasing public demand arising through the 'rave' scene – a music craze involving energetic dancing for hours on end in packed clubs.

Although this drug is not particularly addictive, it can become extremely important, particularly with young people in their social environment. If taken too often, ecstasy loses its potency – and people then look for the same sensation in other drugs. There is as yet little known about the effects of MDMA from long-term use.

Ecstasy is usually available as white, off-white and beige tablets of varying size, and sometimes in capsules containing white powder. It is usually taken by mouth, though it can be injected or snorted (sniffed). The normal dose is 75–100mg, though tablet strength is notoriously unreliable, being 'cut' (diluted) with toxic substances. Some people have been sold dog worming tablets; or, worse still, tablets containing LSD and amphetamines. Ecstasy acts on the body and central nervous system (brain). As with all drugs acting in this way, the psychological effects vary with individual mood, personality and environment.

Commonly, users will take between one and five 'E's over a period of a rave. Generally people report a 'burnout' or feeling 'cabbaged' for one or two days afterwards, characterised by exhaustion, anxiety and depression. Paranoia (suspicion of other people) can occur. Repeated doses of MDMA to try and combat this causes the adrenaline-like effects to continue, with anxiety, panic and insomnia; but the euphoric mental effects fade. It seems there needs to be a drug free period – usually about a week – before these can be experienced again.

Some users mix ecstasy with LSD (candy flipping). This dangerous practice can not only potentiate the risk of bad hallucinogenic experiences but also ensures users are at high risk of suffering from flashbacks (see also LSD). Research shows that flashbacks can occur with MDMA use alone, despite what some may say. Taking alcohol with MDMA can dangerously exacerbate the dehydration that MDMA causes when the body temperature is increased. But users mix alcohol to calm down the amphetamine 'speed' effect of MDMA... Mixing amphetamine with MDMA potentiates the risk of excess stimulation of the heart, circulation and brain, risking convulsions or even death.

Users of ecstasy are guinea pigs in one of the largest unscientific drug trials ever to be undertaken. Not enough is known about the hidden adverse side effects. To date, there have been around sixty deaths in the UK directly ascribed to taking ecstasy. However, with more and more poorly produced 'bathtub' batches, which accidentally contain other hallucinogenic amphetamines, the toll is sure to increase. Death may result from an allergic reaction or from overstimulation of a weak heart. Most deaths have been caused by gross disruption of the natural control of the blood clotting in the body. People who suffer from heart disease, raised blood pressure, glaucoma or epilepsy should never risk taking ecstasy.

MDMA acts on a system of cells in the brain which are responsible for the balance of our emotions. Regular use may cause abnormalities in this system (the serotonin system) resulting in depression or paranoia; but research still continues. MDMA is not related to MPTP – a drug implicated as a cause of Parkinson's disease. There is no evidence to date that MDMA is implicated in the onset of Parkinson's disease in users.

MDMA can be found in the urine for between 2–4 days after use. Both possession and supply of the drug are illegal and carry stiff jail sentences as well as heavy fines.

Effects

Most users experience a 'happy' or 'at peace' feeling that all is right with the world (entactogenesis) and this, coupled with a feeling of 'opening up', an emotional closeness to others (empathogenesis) is responsible for MDMA being labelled as the 'hug drug'. Subtle visual, taste and smell distortions are often experienced. Unfortunately the euphoria that MDMA induces makes it easy for the user to ignore body distress signals. When used in an all-night dance, signals like dehydration, muscle cramps and heat exhaustion are all ignored.

The effects of ecstasy usually take between 30 minutes to one hour to be felt and last for several hours. The physical effects may be likened to a rush of adrenaline. Initial brief nausea, rapid heart rate and increase in blood pressure, dry mouth and throat, pupils dilating, the jaw tightening. There is increased oxygen consumption in the body which gives rise to escalation in body temperature. All these effects are modified by the concurrent onset of feeling euphoric and heightened sensual awareness to touching and stroking.

However, the user will often experience feelings of depression once the peak has worn off, and could take at least 3-4 hours to return to normality. The depression is caused by chemical actions in the brain produced by MDMA and, if the user is hypersensitive to the drug, seemingly a very rare condition, even a minute dose can kill.

Some concern has been voiced that MDMA could attack the liver and cause problems. It is dangerous for people to use ecstasy if they have heart problems or suffer from high blood pressure, asthma or epilepsy, while the use of antidepressants will have an extremely adverse effect. Pregnant women should certainly avoid the use of MDMA.

Signs and symptoms of Ecstasy misuse

- Extremely dilated pupils.
  Will wear off. A move to a darkened room may help.

- Clenched jaw.
  No action needed, the condition will improve as the drug leaves the system.

- Warm skin, excessive perspiration and body odour.
  Drink plenty of non-alcoholic fluids and "chill out" in a cool place.

- Difficulty co-ordinating.
  Avoid dangerous activities, for example driving, crossing busy thoroughfares.

- Mood and behaviour changes, the extent depending on emotional state of the user and environmental conditions.
  Calming reassurance.

- Heat-stroke.
  Cool down, sponge with tepid water and fan. Plenty of non-alcoholic drinks.

- Collapse.
  Check breathing and pulse. If both present place person in recovery position. If not, dial 999 and CPR (see chapter 7).

- Exhaustion and irritability the following day.
  Rest.

Remedies/Treatment

Users of this drug can easily overexert themselves, which will cause loss of body fluid and salt from perspiration – approximately up to one pint in an hour.

Over a lengthy period dehydration can develop, resulting in possible ecstasy-related death. Replacing fluid is essential. Fruit or sport drinks should be supplied for sipping – not alcohol.

Should the person develop cramp-like sensations in arms, legs and back, or complain of dizziness or headaches which could lead to vomiting, they should be removed to a cooler area and cold water sponging should be applied to help lower the temperature.

The person should be placed in the recovery position and arrangements made for removal to hospital. Clear information about the incident, a sample of any vomitus and possible type of drug will assist hospital staff.

GAMMAHYDROXYBUTYRATE
(Gamma-OH, GHB, 'GBH', Liquid E, Liquid X)

Description

Prescribed in the past to relax people about to undergo operations, Gammahydroxybutyrate is both odourless and colourless but has a slightly salty taste. The use of GHB or Gamma-OH, as it is often called, is patchy on the streets. Sometimes suppliers might have some to sell and then people may be encouraged to purchase it. But generally there is not much call for it. So why bother?

Produced in many 'kitchen laboratories', GHB is offered for recreational use as a drug offering a pleasant, alcohol-like effect which is hangover-free. Technically, GHB is a precursor to one of the chemicals present in the brain, gamma-aminobytyric acid (GABA) – which functions as an inhibitor and may cause sedation. The substance was first synthesised in the 1960s by a French researcher interested in the effects of GABA on the brain. GHB has been used in anaesthetics, for the treatment of sleep disorders, to treat withdrawal from alcohol and opiates – and even as an aid to childbirth, because it is said to increase dilation of the cervix.

In the 1980s, GHB was available in health-food stores and often sold to body-builders because it was thought to release growth hormone from the pituitary gland in the brain. It was also promoted to improve sleep. Although GHB is not controlled under the Misuse of Drugs Act, it is classed as a medicine, so that unauthorised manufacture and supply is an offence under the Medicines Act.

Effects

This is another of the 'downer' drugs which has an effect similar to that experienced after alcohol consumption – the more consumed, the worse the result.

The drug is mainly taken by mouth either in liquid or powder form.

78

A usual dose of about 2 to 5 grams has a noticeable effect after 10-30 minutes of ingesting and lasts between 3-4 hours. Like alcohol, GHB reduces inhibitions and causes a sedative and sometimes euphoric effect. However, nausea, vomiting, diarrhoea and stiffness of muscles, disorientation, convulsions and coma have been reported with increased amounts. There is slowing of the heart rate, lowering of body temperature and inco-ordination. Clearly, these dangers will be increased if mixed with other drugs.

The larger the quantity taken, the more unpleasant the results. These include nausea, vomiting, muscle stiffness and a tendency to feel disorientated. Some users will have fits and can collapse. Although no deaths have been reported to date, there have been some very close calls.

One of the main dangers produced by GHB is if the drug is mixed with alcohol or other sedatives. There are reports of psychological and physical dependency, though no tolerance develops. Not enough is known about problems with long-term use.

There is also no guarantee regarding the strength of the drug, which tends to vary wildly from batch to batch. However, it is not illegal to possess GHB.

Signs and symptoms of GHB misuse

- Drowsy, disorientated
  Monitor in case unconsciousness follows.

- Stiff muscles, incoordination
  Avoid driving or operating machinery.

- Drop in body temperature
  Keep in a warm place, wrapped in warm clothing.

- Slow heart rate
  Monitor. Be prepared for CPR.

- Nausea, vomiting
  Prevent choking on vomitus. Place in recovery position if uncon-scious.

- Convulsions
  Clear away harmful objects to avoid person injuring themselves. Keep airway open. Dial 999

- Coma
  Check breathing and pulse. If both are present, place person in recovery position. Dial 999 and give CPR if appropriate (see chapter 7).

Remedies/Treatment

GHB can be compared with the effects of alcohol abuse; the larger the intake, the more serious the reaction. Again, vomiting coupled with fits and collapse require the use of the recovery position and removal to an A&E department of a hospital.

As with all other drugs, a sample of the vomitus should be col-lected and sent with the patient to hospital for analysis. Monitoring the person's condition is essential.

HALLUCINOGENIC MUSHROOMS
(Magic Mushrooms, Mushies, 'Shrooms, Liberty Caps)

Description

The ancient Aztecs knew of and used 'sacred intoxicants' or hallu-cinogenics in the paneolus or psilocybe mushroom families, while other cultures – notably American Indians and the far-northern European tribal peoples – have ceremonies based around the use of hallucinogenic fungi, often mediated through the 'shaman' or priest. These connections, together with the ready availability of a supply, literally, there for the picking, have made 'magic mushrooms' espe-cially attractive to travelling people and New Age communities.

There are several varieties of 'magic mushrooms' which grow wild in the United Kingdom. The active ingredients they contain are psilocin and psilocybin, both hallucinogenics with similar properties to LSD. The most common and hence popular mushroom used on the street is the Liberty Cap (psilocybe semilanceata). These are har-vested in the autumn.

The mushrooms are either eaten raw, cooked or brewed in a drink. They may be dried and stored for later use. An effect similar to a mild LSD dose is experienced when about 30 mushrooms are taken orally. There is excitement, euphoria and visual hallucinations. The user often feels as if they are floating up in the air, looking down on them-selves. However, as with LSD, a 'bad trip' may occur. A magic mush-room trip lasts about half as long as an LSD trip – about four hours. A smaller dose of magic mushrooms may just cause relaxation and euphoria without an hallucinogenic 'trip'.

On the downside, magic mushrooms cause nausea, dizziness, increased heart rate and blood pressure and dilated pupils. Tolerance develops rapidly; and, unless a week or so is left before repeating the experience, more and more mushrooms would be needed to produce the same effect. If a bad trip is experienced, flashbacks may later occur when, out of the blue, the user relives the trip with all its vivid memories. Although perhaps lasting only a few minutes, these

81

episodes can leave the person feeling anxious and distressed.

By far the biggest dangers arise if the mushrooms used are not 'magic mushrooms' but one of the many varieties of poisonous fungi, such as Death Cap which looks very similar to the Liberty Cap.

It is against the law to be in possession of psilocybin, but in their natural form 'magic mushrooms' are not illegal. However, they do become illegal if they are dried, crushed and prepared into a 'brew', at which point police prosecutions are highly likely. Psilocybin and psilocin are Class A controlled drugs.

Effects

An LSD-like trip, with hallucinations, distorted perceptions and sensations such as flying or floating 'out of body'.

The mushrooms can produce panic attacks if frequent or large doses are taken. This condition settles best if reassurance can be provided by another person close at hand.

Since judgement is severely impaired, accidents can happen; particularly if the user attempts to drive a car whilst under the influence of 'magic mushrooms'.

The most dangerous effect is through incorrect identification of the substance in the wild. Similar mushrooms can produce strong stomach pains, diarrhoea and vomiting or liver failure resulting in death.

If sickness or vomiting occurs, hospital intervention must be sought immediately, and a sample should be obtained if possible to take with the patient to the hospital.

Signs and symptoms of hallucinogenic Mushroom misuse

- Euphoria.
  Avoid dangerous situations while state persists.

- Distorted ideas of shapes and colours.
  If patient is disturbed by sensations offer calming reassurance.

- Hallucinations.
  If patient is disturbed by sensations offer calming reassurance.

- Detached feelings as if looking down from above.
  If patient is disturbed by the effect, offer calming reassurance.

- Dizziness.
  May be followed by fainting.

- Stomach pains.
  Seek medical advice if symptom continues.

- Nausea, vomiting.
  Ensure no choking follows. Put in recovery position if unconscious.

- Diarrhoea.
  Seek medical advice if continues.

Remedies/Treatment

In the event of a bad 'trip', paranoia is quite common and requires plenty of reassurance. If drowsy, use of the recovery position is advisable in order to prevent vomitus inhalation. Should vomiting continue, it may be due to using similar poisonous mushrooms by mistake. Seek immediate medical help.

HEROIN
(Junk, Horse, Smack, Skag)

Description

The medicinal value of the poppy is first described in the works of
Hippocrates, although seeds and capsules of poppies have been found
at Stone Age sites. Opiate alkaloids extracted from the capsule of the
opium poppy comprise morphine, codeine, thebaine, papaverine, nar-
cotine, narceine and laudanum. The search to produce other strong
opiates for medicinal use led to the discovery of diamorphine or
heroin in 1874. Other synthetic opioids used as painkillers include
pethedine, dipipanone (Diconal) and methadone (Physeptone). The
latter drug is usually prescribed as a less addictive substitute in cases
of opiate dependence.

In fact, heroin was originally used to treat morphine addiction
before it was appreciated that it 'cured' morphine addiction only by
substituting itself as the addicting agent... It is mainly used now for
the treatment of acutely painful conditions but its use is controlled
under the Misuse of Drugs Act, making it a Class A drug which it is
illegal to supply or possess without a prescription.

Formerly dispensed to registered addicts on prescription, heroin
started to appear for use on the street in the 1960s when younger users
began obtaining it illegally from GPs. By the mid-1970s, a significant
black market was growing to import illicitly manufactured heroin
from Turkey, Iran, Afghanistan, India, China, Thailand and Burma.
More recently, heroin imported from Columbia has been appearing on
the street.

It is worth mentioning that if heroin is in short supply, addicts can
fall back on some cough mixtures such as Gee's Linctus, which contain codeine, morphine or opium. Anti-diarrhoea medicines containing opiates, such as kaolin & morphine mixture, are another favourite.
Pure heroin is a white fluffy powder that dissolves almost instantly
in water. Most illegal supplies of heroin come as a powder ranging in
colour from off-white to mid-brown. Street heroin is 'cut' or mixed

commonly with sugars, talcum powder, quinine, ground glass or almost any imaginable powder. It is sold wrapped in a small, specially folded paper parcel – a 'wrap'. Heroin is not very effective when taken by mouth, as it is poorly absorbed by the intestine. Instead, it is absorbed much more directly into the bloodstream via the blood vessels lining the nose, or via the lungs. The powder may be sniffed like cocaine, smoked in cigarettes; or, by using a small tube or drinking straw, inhaled as fumes produced by heating it on tin foil, a spoon or flattened can. When heated, it turns to a brown sticky liquid stream. This 'stream' is kept flowing back and forth, enabling the fumes to come off it slowly ('chasing the dragon'). Many other home made devices, or paraphernalia which allow the fumes to be concentrated, abound.

Finally, heroin may be injected directly into the blood vessels and this method is favoured if the user does not want to waste any of the precious supply in smoke. Prior to injecting, the powder is dissolved in water or lemon juice in a spoon or bottle cap by warming it over a flame before drawing it up into a syringe.

Heroin is being promoted insidiously nowadays as a harmless way of 'coming down' from stimulant drugs such as amphetamines and ecstasy to round off a weekend's rave. Of course, suppliers are hopeful that those trying it will find the experience desirable enough to repeat on its own.

Heroin can be detected in the urine from 1-2 days after use. Compare this with up to 20 days for some other drugs, and there is an added incentive to switch. Used sensibly, heroin is not in fact the most dangerous of drugs; however, the authorities look on its use extremely seriously. If a user is found to be in possession, he or she can get a heavy sentence as well as unlimited fines. For those supplying the drug, conviction can carry with it life imprisonment and forfeiture of property and assets. In some countries, notably Malaysia and Iran, possession of heroin for supply carries an automatic death penalty.

Effects

The effects of heroin on the body are basically the same regardless of route but the delivery methods have different speeds of onset and their own intrinsic risks. As we have said, heroin can be taken in one of three different ways:

a) Smoking, which penetrates the body at a slower rate and can therefore be controlled more easily.

b) Sniffing (often called 'snorting') which enables the complete dose to enter the system immediately, thus increasing the danger of overdosing almost as much as injecting.

c) Injecting the drug – which produces the highest risk factor.

If the third method is used, the drug will reach the brain almost immediately the substance is injected, increasing the risk of overdose. Heroin injections are very rarely administered under aseptic conditions, therefore all kinds of of impurities could enter the bloodstream which could cause infections at the injection sites and lead to fatal septicaemia (blood poisoning), where the infection has spread around the whole body. Frequent injections can cause damage to the veins and precipitate thrombosis (blood clotting) as well as increase the risk of abscess formation.

The user is continually forced to seek new injection sites, which may include the inside of the arms, legs, groin, penis and even the eyes.

Many drug users are obliged to share syringes, a practice which increases the risk of contracting HIV or hepatitis infection. The former can eventually lead to Aids, while the latter can kill from the damage it has caused to the liver.

The initial experience of heroin is not always pleasant. There can be nausea and vomiting. These unpleasant reactions fade with repeated use. Users experience a rush of pleasure as the drug enters the system, then a sleepy, pleasant euphoria and a relaxed detachment from all stress, pain and anxiety. There is little interference with sensation, motor skills or intellect at low doses, but at higher doses a sleepy, drowsy contentment comes over the user, excessive doses producing loss of consciousness. Blood vessels are dilated (giving a feeling of warmth). The breathing rate slows, there is suppression of the cough reflex, the heart rate slows. Bowel activity is reduced, resulting in constipation. The pupils in the eyes also contract.

The pleasant effects of opiates soon give rise to psychological dependence. These feelings have a reinforcing effect of their own but the user may also miss these effects as they wear off. They may need to take heroin more frequently in order to feel 'normal'(see chapter 2, p20, 'Reward dependence and harm avoidance'). Tolerance then develops easily – an increased dose or change in method of administration is needed to produce the same effects. Injection into the veins does not waste any of the drug and is the obvious progression. It makes the effect almost instantaneous, producing a short-lived, pleasurable 'rush'. On average, a dependent user might take ¼ gram or more each day. After as little as a few weeks on frequent doses, physical dependence results. The user continues to take heroin in order to stay 'normal', and avoid the unpleasant effects of withdrawal.

Withdrawal of the drug from the habitual user causes shakes, yawning, restlessness, sleeplessness, gastric upsets, dilated pupils, muscle and bone ache, a rapid heartbeat, high blood pressure, runny nose and eyes and sweating with an intense cold feeling over the body (going 'cold turkey'). These withdrawal symptoms are very unpleasant but not life threatening and generally fade after seven to ten days, although a feeling of weakness and loss of wellbeing may last for several months.

Fatal overdoses can happen when heroin users take their 'usual dose' after a break during which tolerance has faded, or if a new supply is stronger than expected. Death from injecting heroin may not be entirely due to the respiratory and cardiac depression from the drug itself but often to adulterants in the street drug, such as quinine which interferes with the control of the heartbeat, or because the user is also taking other depressant drugs, like alcohol, at the same time.

Signs and symptoms of Heroin misuse

- Lethargy, drowsiness
  Monitor in case unconsciousness follows.

- Constricted pupils
  No action needed.

- Mood change, euphoria or dysphoria
  No action needed.

- Redness and raw nostrils from inhaling
  May need to seek medical advice.

- Scars or needle tracks on inner arms or almost any site from injecting
  These may be infected. There is a risk of hepatitis and HIV if needle sharing.

- Slurred speech
  General coordination may also be affected. Avoid driving and using machinery.

- Nausea, vomiting
  Ensure no choking follows. Put in recovery position if unconscious.

- Cessation of respiration
  Dial 999 Check pulse and commence resuscitation.

- Convulsions (rare)
  Clear away harmful objects to avoid person injuring himself or herself. Keep airway open. Dial 999.

Remedies/Treatment

The misuse of this drug will produce mood and behavioural changes, which, at times can be very disturbing to the user. It would therefore not be advisable to send the person to hospital unless he/she develops breathing difficulties. Reassurance and a calm, informative approach are necessary. Any movement outside the safety of the present location can become very frightening and produce severe panic attacks. Noisy hospitals and persistent questions should be avoided. Reassurance that the person is not going mad and that everything will eventually get back to normality should take priority.

LSD
(Acid, Trips, Tabs, Window Panes)

Description

In 1938, lysergic acid diethylamide (LSD) was the 25th in a series of molecules synthesised from lysergic acid by a large drug company in search of a new drug to be used as a stimulant in psychotherapy. Hence the number 25 sometimes appended to the initials! It is derived from ergot, a fungus found growing naturally on grasses, whose poisonous effects include hallucinations. The drug was shelved after unpromising preliminary test results on animals, although the US military continued researching it as a potential nerve agent. In 1943, a laboratory scientist who was investigating the drug series accidentally ingested a minute quantity of LSD, one of the most potent drugs ever discovered. The first 'trip' was taken, and his experience was documented in the archives.

In the 1950s, there was a move among psychologists and therapists to use mind-expanding drugs to facilitate treatment of disturbed personalities and release repressed thoughts and feelings. LSD was legally manufactured to supply this clinical work. But research again failed to establish LSD as a useful therapeutic drug and its licence was restricted by law to be used only in experiments carried out by 'approved and responsible practitioners'. However, even whilst restricted under the Misuse of Drugs Act, its illegal use began to grow, especially associated with the hippy movement in California where it emerged in the 'sixties as a drug openly promoted by fashionable artists, writers and academics such as Dr Timothy Leary, with claims that it could 'blow your mind' and help you 'find yourself'. (Leary later spent time in prison for supplying LSD). Psychedelic music and light shows helped to expand its effects and popularity among young club goers, and at rock festivals.

In 1973, LSD was classified as a controlled drug under Class A of the Misuse of Drugs Act, so that supply carries a maximum penalty of life imprisonment plus a fine, and possession seven years imprisonment plus a fine.

Today, LSD is less associated with the typical quasi-religious groups of users of the 1960s, who have moved on to transcendental meditation and other self-induced 'highs' as their preferred method of achieving spiritual enlightenment. LSD is now promoted as just another way to get 'stoned'. It has found favour once again with young people involved in the dance culture, seeking new experiences through altered states of perception. Typically they might also be taking amphetamines and ecstasy.

When synthesised, LSD in its pure state is a fine white powder. Because it is so powerful, it is diluted many times in an alcohol solution, so in theory it becomes easier to measure out a desired dose, typically to drop onto a sugar cube. In practice, though, the solution is more normally sprayed onto large sheets of absorbent paper, pegged on a line. The blotting paper is marked out in 5mm squares, each of which carries an attractive, seemingly harmless printed design. (And no, this doesn't tell you what kind of 'trip' you're going to have! The different designs help the dealer with 'stock control', since tabs have a limited shelf life...) The alcohol evaporates, leaving the LSD impregnated in the paper. There is a snag – more of the crudely sprayed-on solution drains to the bottom squares, so they contain more LSD than those on the upper part of the sheet. The 'better' street drug factories cut these off and discard them or sell them as doubles or super LSDs.

Taking the LSD is easily accomplished by placing the squares of blotting paper on the tongue and letting saliva dissolve it off. The usual dose of LSD on the squares is between 50-75 micrograms, but doses vary. Ingesting 150mcg produces a full-blown trip. LSD may less commonly come in capsules, microdots, small squares of gelatine or even tablets. There never were any 'active tattoos' either – those were a street myth.

Granny (or her Grandson) Takes a Trip...

The effects of LSD are usually described as a 'trip' because it is like taking a journey to another place. With no other drug is it so true that the effect is dependent on the initial psychological state, emotions and expectations of the user; LSD is like playing with fire. Once started on a trip, it can't be stopped.

Half an hour after being taken, colours appear more brilliant, moving objects leave traces behind them and when the eyes are closed, patterns can be seen. Visual hallucinations become more intense after an hour and figures and shapes appear from nowhere, at which time users no longer need to shut their eyes to see patterns. Distortion of hearing occurs. At the peak of a full trip, time is slowed almost to a standstill and trippers feel they are in a different world, although generally the user knows these effects are unreal. They have impaired judgement, sometimes feeling total fear and panic at being in a terrifying nightmare which has become 'real'. Unpleasant reactions are more likely if the user is unstable, depressed or anxious. They may suffer bad hallucinations and paranoia – a 'bad trip'. After 8-12 hours the effects fade, but the 'tripper' is often left feeling depressed and, if they have had a bad trip, anxious and distressed. Even after months, 'flashbacks' may occur when, out of the blue the user relives a past trip with all its vivid memories. Although perhaps lasting only a few minutes, these episodes can leave the person anxious and distressed. LSD flashbacks are reported more frequently when the person is smoking cannabis.

LSD is an illegal drug. If someone is found to be in possession, they can be imprisoned for up to seven years with an unlimited fine attached. Supplying the drug can lead to life imprisonment as well as a heavy fine. Tests can identify LSD in the urine up to 2-3 days after use.

Effects

The principal effects are hallucinogenic, or 'psychedelic'. The drug acts on the mind, about which very little is known, to produce bizarre sensations, visions and altered, dream-like states.

If the user has any underlying mental problems, this drug can trigger delusions, schizophrenia-like states or paranoia.

People can go into severe anxiety states or attacks of panic, not only while under the influence of the drug but for quite a time after the effects have worn off. It can also produce personality changes or impair judgement which makes it highly unsafe to drive. (Some deaths caused by falling from high buildings have been attributed to LSD users believing they could fly.)

The physical effects of LSD are mild, including rise in body temperature, 'goose bumps' and dilation of the pupils.

A number of users suffer psychological after-effects. 'Acid casualties' undergo a permanent personality change and may suffer psychotic illness, the latter being more common among regular users in whom LSD brings out an otherwise hidden psychosis.

There is no evidence to suggest that physical dependence ever develops, but tolerance is rapidly built up. Without a break of around three days, a much larger dose of LSD is needed to produce the same effect again.

Not enough research has been carried out to produce any reliable evidence that LSD causes permanent brain damage or genetic damage to future children.

Signs and symptoms of LSD misuse

- Extremely dilated pupils.
  This will pass as drug leaves the system. A move to a darkened room may help.

- Warm skin, excessive perspiration and body odour.
  Plenty of non-alcoholic drinks. Take into a cool place. Avoid strenuous activity for long periods.

- Distorted sense of sight, hearing, touch; distorted image of self and time perception.
  If disturbed by sensations, offer calming reassurance.

- Mood and behaviour changes, the extent depending on emotional state of the user and environmental conditions.
  If disturbed, reassure, avoid dangerous situations. Monitor.

- Unpredictable flashback episodes even long after withdrawal (although these are rare).
  Reassure that this will improve with time.

Remedies/Treatment

The use of this drug will produce mood and behavioural changes which, at times can be very disturbing to the user.

It would therefore not be advisable to send the person to hospital unless they develop breathing difficulties. Reassurance and a calm, informative approach will be necessary. Any movement outside the safety of the present location can become very frightening and produce severe panic attacks. Noisy hospitals and persistent questions should be avoided. Reassurance should be given that the person is not going mad and that everything will get back to normal eventually.

METHADONE
(Script, Meth, Linctus, Physeptone)

Description

Methadone is a synthetic opiate first invented in the 1940s as a long-acting pain killer. It may be injected or taken orally. Its use as a painkiller was never really successful nor popular, however. It can be taken in a linctus as a cough suppressant, but is more commonly used as a legal, supervised substitute for heroin, when heroin or other opiate addicts are trying to reduce the amount and risks of illicit opiate drug use or trying to withdraw altogether from opiates. Methadone helps to reduce withdrawal symptoms from heroin without causing a worse habit. The drug substitutes itself in the body for heroin and blocks the effects of heroin if heroin is taken. Methadone is prescribed as an oral medicine which is taken once a day. The medicine is made up to be intensely irritant if injected, in an attempt to prevent misuse – the problem being, that an addict will abuse any substance, however uncomfortable, in order to get a 'fix'...

Effects

The high from methadone is less intense than from heroin – there is no rush or hit – but it is longer-lasting and users tend not to crave as much. They can get used to life without a buzz and may become drug free with additional help. It takes care to replace the street opiate doses with methadone, because so often the true dose of heroin taken is not clear from the amount of street heroin the user says he or she has been taking. Methadone also takes up to four days for a steady level to be achieved in the body.

Users complain that methadone withdrawal can be worse than coming off heroin; but the aim, if coming off the drug altogether, is to reduce the dose very slowly until no further supplies are needed. Development of further tolerance to methadone itself is slow.

However, if users have reduced their dose or stopped taking the methadone for a while so that tolerance is low and then return to street opiates of unknown strength or even to the higher doses of methadone, they may overdose.

Methadone is normally dispensed from specialist drug dependency units. It can appear illegally on the streets from these sources, as users 'exchange' it for other drugs. On the street, it is often mixed with alcohol. Methadone is a Class A drug; it is legal to possess it on prescription. The maximum sentence for unlawful possession is seven years in prison and an unlimited fine. The maximum sentence for supplying methadone is life imprisonment and an unlimited fine.

Signs and symptoms of Methadone misuse

Methadone is usually taken whilst withdrawing from an opiate habit, and hence, under supervision.

- Controlled, levelled emotions

- Reduction of physical pain
  Check that this is not masking any injuries

- Drowsiness
  Monitor in case unconsciousness follows. Prevent from driving or operating machinery.

- Heavy feeling in arms & legs
  No action needed.

- Slower, shallower breathing
  Monitor in case breathing stops and be prepared to give CPR.

- Dry mouth, eyes & nose
  Frequent sips of non-alcoholic drinks.

- Nausea
  Be aware vomiting might follow.

- Sweating, flushed skin
  Check other causes. An infection may be causing this.

- Itching
  Seek medical advice if troublesome.

- Constipation
  Plenty of fluids and high fibre diet.

- Small pupils
  No action needed.

Remedies/Treatment

Although the recognisable symptoms are similar to those of heroin, the time taken before going into unconsciousness will be longer. The person will become drowsy and eventually go into unconsciousness from overdosing. This again will require hospital intervention and monitoring while waiting for the ambulance.

OPIUM

Description

Opium is obtained from the latex or milky juice exuded from the unripe capsule or seed head of the poppy flower, Papaver Somniferum, which is grown for the purposes of drug production mainly in India, Thailand, Turkey and the Asiatic provinces – although opium-producing poppies flourish happily in British gardens. The brown coloured, soft, sticky resin obtained from the latex is dried to a powder which contains a mixture of natural opiates, most important of which are morphine and codeine. These substances have painkilling properties.

Since as long ago as the 1st century AD, and probably a lot earlier, opium has been used medicinally when swallowed in one form or another. Serious addiction problems became apparent in the 17th century, however, when western traders in this compact, easily transported, non-perishable commodity introduced opium smoking into China, where it rapidly got out of control. By the mid-19th century, England too was beginning to realise the depth of its home-grown opium problem. Even the great fictional detective, Sherlock Holmes, is known to have become hooked! Popular opium-containing remedies such as Laudanum could be purchased easily over the counter, alongside food and spirits. Usually, the opiate was bought or prescribed for some kind of common ailment, and addiction would begin insidiously with frequent, innocent use leading to eventual dependance.

Opium is not very fashionable nowadays, and is seen only sporadically on the street. It is sold as a powder or dark brown resinous solid and is injected after heating it to melting point on tin foil, eaten raw, or smoked in special pipes.

Effects

Opium produces a feeling of relaxation, contentment and euphoria. The user feels no need for company and is happy to be left alone. In very low doses excitement may occur, but this is unusual. With higher doses there is slowing of the pulse, shallower breathing, drowsiness and eventually dreamful sleep. Overdose causes coma and death as respiration is depressed and stopped.

The habitual use of opium produces tolerance whereby increasing amounts of the drug are required to produce the same effect. Dependence occurs and the habit is continued not so much because the taking of opium gives pleasure, but because its lack produces the worst feelings of misery.

Acute withdrawal from opium addiction causes perspiration, runny nose and eyes, restless sleep, lack of sleep, dilated pupils, goosebumps, twitching, abdominal pains, retching, vomiting and diarrhoea. Breathing rate increases and blood pressure rises.

Signs and symptoms of opium misuse

- Lethargy, drowsiness
  Monitor in case unconsciousness follows.

- Constricted pupils
  No action needed.

- Mood change, euphoria or dysphoria
  No action needed.

- Scars or needle tracks on inner arms or almost any site from injecting
  These may be infected. There is a risk of hepatitis and HIV if needle sharing.

- Slurred speech
  General co-ordination also may be affected. Avoid driving and using machinery.

- Nausea, vomiting
  Ensure no choking follows. Put in recovery position if unconscious.

- Cessation of respiration
  Dial 999, check pulse and commence resuscitation.

- Convulsions (rare)
  Clear away harmful objects to avoid person injuring themselves. Keep airway open. Dial 999

- Use of paraphernalia, including syringes, needles, spoons, bottle caps, eye droppers, rubber tubing, tin foil.

Remedies/Treatment

The opium user who has overdosed will require hospital treatment, therefore medical assistance is required. In case of unconsciousness, the person should be placed in the recovery position and carefully monitored in case breathing and pulse stops. CPR must then be carried out, having first dialled 999.

OVER-THE-COUNTER DRUGS
(OTCs)

Description

Over-the-counter medications are available for a variety of symptoms and ills. Many are available in tablets or oral liquid form. All these preparations can be obtained without a prescription, and some are subject to misuse. There are two classes of over-the-counter medicines: those which can only be sold in registered pharmacies (pharmacy-only medicines) and those on the general sale list (GSL medicines) which can also be purchased in other shops when certain conditions apply, for example where the dose or number of doses sold is small.

Drug misusers may turn to any of these medicines when cash or supplies of their usual choice of drug are low.

Those over-the-counter medications which are most popularly abused are either in the antihistamine group, the opiate group or the sympathomimetic group.

The antihistamine group contains medicines which are sold to combat allergic conditions such as hayfever, allergy rashes and insect bites. In particular, these antihistamines are frequently mixed by drug abusers with alcohol, so that an effect which is almost hallucinogenic is achieved. However, many of the more recent antihistamines will not cause these effects. One of the most popular antihistamines misused is cyclizine – which was, together with dipipanone, a constituent of diconal, an opiate type drug which is now only prescribable under a special Home Office licence. It is popular to crush up cyclizine tablets and inject them with methadone in an attempt to reproduce the high obtained from diconal.

The second group of over-the-counter medications contains opiates. These are commonly preparations used to combat diarrhoea or suppress cough, and some painkillers. The main ingredient sought after is the codeine present in many of them. Paracetamol is also often included in many of these remedies, so that if the user takes too much in an attempt to get a high from the codeine, they may also overdose on paracetamol and cause potentially fatal liver damage.

The third popular group of over-the-counter medicines is the sympathomimetics. These are present in many cold remedies used to dry up secretions which cause a runny nose and chesty cough. These medicines are related to amphetamines and as such are misused in an attempt to reproduce stimulation and euphoria.

Many of the cold remedies contain all three types of medication, so it is often difficult to predict which effect will occur from one of them. Misusers are happy to give any of them a try and experience eventually tells them which brand or combination gives them the effect they are looking for.

Effects

Various, according to specific drug. Anything from incoherence to drowsiness and even death. Not always obvious from the label!

Signs and symptoms of OTC drug misuse

Depends on the type or combination of medicines taken. Try to establish which drug has been taken. General symptoms include:

- Confusion
  Keep away from harm and reassure.

- Inco-ordination
  Avoid driving and using machinery.

- Drowsiness
  Monitor in case unconsciousness follows.

- Over-excitement
  Avoid dangerous incidents.

Remedies/Treatment

Should overdosing be suspected, the person must be removed to hospital. If possible, the medication or empty bottle should be sent with the casualty as well as other samples (especially vomitus). Breathing and pulse must be monitored.

PRESCRIPTION-ONLY MEDICINES
(POMs)

Description

Drug misusers may turn to any of these medicines when money is short, or when street supplies of their usual drug are low or of noticeably poor quality at the time.

Almost any prescribed medicine can find its way onto the street. Many prescribed medications are abused by the person for whom they have been prescribed. Typically, the benzodiazepines may be misused by the person for whom they have been prescribed because they have become addicted to them. It is not uncommon for that person to obtain more of the medication than they actually need and to sell off the excess in order to buy other street drugs. There is also a tendency for some GPs to routinely over-prescribe.

Strong opiate-type analgesics such as dihydrocodeine, co-proxamol containing dextropropoxyphene, co-dydramol containing dihydrocodeine and cocodamol containing codeine have all found their way onto the street. Hypnotics on the street have all mostly found their way from legal sources such as medical suppliers and prescribed medication. Salbutamol used in asthma inhalers is reputed to cause a euphoric effect if inhaled in great quantities.

Many street drug users will try any prescription-only drug if they can get it, regardless of its effect – they are just looking for a buzz.

Effects

Various, according to specific drug.

Signs and symptoms of POM drug misuse

Depends on the type or combination of POM taken. Try to establish which drug has been taken. Symptoms may include:

- Confusion
  Keep away from harm and reassure.

- Incoordination
  Avoid driving and using machinery.

- Drowsiness
  Monitor in case unconsciousness follows.

- Over-excitement
  Avoid dangerous incidents

Remedies/Treatment

Should overdosing take place, the person must be removed to hospital. If possible, the medication or empty bottle should be sent with the casualty as well as other samples (vomitus). Breathing and pulse must be monitored. If the GP 's details are known, it is advisable to contact them for exact information about any drugs prescribed.

SOLVENTS AND VOLATILE SUBSTANCES
(Glue, Bute, Gas, other trade names)

Description

The fumes from commonly available solvents and volatile substances can be inhaled in order to produce a similarly intoxicating effect to that of alcohol or anaesthetics. The 'high' effects follow quickly because absorption through the lungs into the bloodstream is a quick process. Similarly, the effect wears off quickly; and, to keep high, it is necessary to keep inhaling.

The craze is not new; there were crazes for inhaling laughing gas (nitrous oxide) and ether in the 19th century; addiction was an occupational hazard among dentists and anaesthetists, who could hardly avoid the fumes in any case.

Any of the following chemicals may be inhaled: benzene, carbon tetrachloride, chloroform, ethyl ether, ketones including acetone, mexane, naphtha, toluene, trichlorethylene, trichlorophane. These are frequently found in fast-drying glues, contact adhesives, paints, paint thinners, petroleum products, dry cleaning fluids, mothballs, nail varnish remover and in many aerosol sprays.

Use is often experimental in youths between the ages of 11 to 16, more commonly in small groups, where the craze might affect one neighbourhood for a while and then move on. Solutions are often poured onto a cuff or sleeve and the fumes inhaled. Thicker substances may be put inside a bag (crisp or small freezer bag) and the bag held over the mouth and nose. Larger bags (such as dustbin liner bags) may be used which can be fitted over the whole head. It is the use of these larger receptacles which can give rise to suffocation and death if the user becomes unconscious with their head inside the bag.

The propellant from aerosols, typically butane lighter fuel, can be sprayed directly into the mouth. Problems may arise here because the gas cools as it rapidly escapes and as it hits the larynx, it causes reflex spasm and blocks the normal airway. Suffocation results. When solvents or volatile substance misusers get 'out of their head' on the fumes, they experience feelings of dizziness, unreality, slurred speech, double vision, or they may just feel nauseous and drowsy. Behaviour may become boisterous or depressive depending on how they felt before sniffing or what result they were expecting. Hallucinations are not uncommon. Effects disappear within 15 to 45 minutes when sniffing is stopped. The sniffer may be left with a 'hangover' – headache, sore throat, runny nose, poor concentration, feeling nauseous and perhaps drowsy.

Unfortunately, because many of the substances are highly inflammable and some sniffers use heat to increase the amount of fumes given off, there is always a risk of fire.

There is no evidence of significant physical tolerance nor dependence, though obvious psychological dependence may develop, also addiction to the culture with attendant risk of exposure to other drugs – while there are various unwanted social consequences of the glue sniffing culture, such as truancy and minor crime, to contend with.

The Intoxicating Substances (Supply) Act of 1985 makes it an offence for a person to supply or offer to supply solvents to people under the age of 16 when the supplier knows or has reasonable cause to believe that the substance is likely to be used for the purpose of intoxication. Solvent possession or misuse is not in itself a criminal offence, but a number of manufacturers have recognised the problem and are working to introduce alternative products.

Effects

Solvent inhaling is often positively compared with alcohol intake. Users will feel unable to concentrate, will be unsteady on their feet and may become drowsy. Others may experience hallucinations and even apparitions which, in turn, will produce some panic feelings.

Drug inhalation induces a very rapid effect which can cause the user to feel uplifted, vigorous, hale and hearty and euphoric – all of which can induce a 'rush'. However, this effect will rapidly diminish; therefore frequent sniffs will be repeated in order to re-experience this 'rush'.

Death in young solvent users is on the increase. The heart will be adversely affected through physical exertion or panic and fright which can lead to heart failure. Some users will spray aerosol directly into the mouth. This can cause the throat to freeze, and the user suffocates.

Suffocation can be caused by the substance being sprayed into plastic bags which are then placed over mouth and nose and inhaled, the sniffer then losing consciousness. If the user chooses to apply this method and sniffs solvents in an out-of-the-way place, they may not be found in time if their condition deteriorates.

The long-term effects of hydrocarbon chemicals on the body's nervous system, liver and kidneys are not clearly known. Various products bought over-the-counter may contain dangerous chemicals which the user may be unaware of. These can lead to life-threatening situations, perhaps after many years. Benzene, for instance, is a known cancer-causing agent.

Any long-term effects on the brain may be difficult to assess and might also be due to the oxygen deprivation that occurs during the process involved in sniffing.

Signs and symptoms of Solvent misuse

- Substance odour on breath and clothes.
  Try to identify the solvent used.

- Runny nose.
  No action needed. Seek medical advice if it persists.

- Soreness around nose & mouth.
  Seek medical advice.

- Watering eyes.
  Eyes may need irrigating with clean water if solvent is in them.

- Breathing difficulties.
  Move into fresh air and seek immediate medical help.

- Irregular pulse.
  Move into fresh air and seek immediate medical help.

- Drowsiness or unconsciousness.
  Move into fresh air. Check breathing and pulse. If both present place person in recovery position. If not dial 999 and commence CPR.

- Poor muscle control.
  Avoid dangerous activities such as driving, crossing roads.

- Presence of bags or rags containing dry plastic cement or other solvent at home, in locker at school or at work.
  Point these out.

- Suffocation.
  Dial 999 and commence CPR.

Remedies/Treatment

People using solvents usually do so in hidden places, away from crowds. If plastic bags are found to be placed over the head, they should be removed fast. There will hopefully be evidence of the substance used, such as cans, aerosol tins etc, The person should be taken to a source of fresh air and, if already unconscious but breathing, put into the recovery position. The situation will require urgent removal to hospital so 999 should be dialled. If necessary, CPR should be commenced, taking care to use protective masks if available.

CLASSES OF DRUGS
(MISUSE OF DRUGS ACT, 1971)

CLASS A	CLASS B	CLASS C
Heroin	Cannabis (resin or leaves)	Steroids
Methadone	Amphetamine (speed)	Tranquillisers
Opium	Barbiturates	(e.g. Benzodiazepine)
Morphine	Codeine	(when used non-medicinally)
Cocaine/ crack		Mild amphetamines
LSD		Certain painkillers
Psylocibin (processed		
magic mushrooms*)		
Ecstacy		
Any Class B drug which is		
injected		

Note: It is not illegal to possess or to consume magic mushrooms - only to prepare or process them in any way, e.g., to dry them or make an infusion or tea from them.

MAXIMUM PENALTIES FOR INDICTABLE OFFENCES (i.e., those heard in the Crown Court)

Possession:	*Possession:*	*Possession:*
7 years imprisonment/	5 years imprisonment/	2 years imprisonment/
fine or both	fine or both	fine or both
Supplying:	*Supplying:*	*Supplying:*
Life imprisonment/	14 years imprisonment/	5 years imprisonment/
fine or both	fine or both	fine or both

Note: Fines in a Crown Court are unspecified and are at the discretion of the judge. Suppliers' property may be confiscated in lieu.

MAXIMUM PENALTIES FOR SUMMARY OFFENCES, i.e., those heard in a Magistrates Court.

Possession:	*Possession:*	*Possession:*
6 months imprisonment/	3 months imprisonment/	3 months imprisonment/
£2000 fine or both	£500 fine or both	£200 fine or both
Supplying:	*Supplying:*	*Supplying:*
6 months imprisonment/	6 months imprisonment/	6 months imprisonment/
£2000 fine or both	£2000 fine or both	£500 fine or both

Figure 6.

Please note, the list above shows the maximum penalties for possession and supply in each category. In practice the penalties, especially for personal use, are generally much less, and will depend on such factors as the quantities involved, previous criminal record and personal circumstances as much as the attitude of any particular magistrate or judge.

5

Drug Mixes
('Snidey Drugs')

'Quality control' scarcely exists when we are dealing with, or buying, street drugs. There is absolutely no guarantee that the user will get what he/she expects. Drugs can be adulterated, particularly those illegal drugs which come in pill or powder form. Rubbishy additions and adulterants are often mixed with the foundation substance and these in themselves can be very dangerous, since it is difficult to know exactly what a powder or pill contains without laboratory tests.

Drug combinations are often unknown quantities which can produce dangerous consequences. In particular, overdose cases when analysed have been found to contain mixtures of sedatives, often mixed with alcohol.

Snidey drugs can be split into two distinct groups. The first contains a substance which is an actual drug but its content is not what the user has asked for. The second group consists of substances which are not drugs at all.

For example, ecstasy often turns out to be an amphetamine or ketamine or LSD, or even a combination of a number of different drugs. Amphetamines may actually contain a small amount of the real substance but, to give the so-called drug bulk and to make it look like the authentic drug, will have been mixed with any convincing-looking white powder – for example, milk powder or glucose.

Dealers want to make maximum amounts of profit from the dance drug market. Those who don't care about their customers are not averse to selling ketamine as ecstasy, if they happen to have it.

Ketamine can be used medically to induce rapid anaesthesia but its use can be complicated by important adverse effects including hallu-cinations. Dealers hope this latter, adverse side effect will 'satisfy' their customers – but many of those people slumped in dark corners of any large dance party not knowing who they are, what they are doing and unable to feel anything have been sold ketamine – they have been 'Ketted'!

Snidey drugs tend to be very costly in relation to the rubbish they often contain. The effect of snidey drugs is not always what is expected and they can produce seriously bad mental or physical reactions.

One way or another, mixing drugs is often far more dangerous than using a particular single drug – especially if the substance is doubtful. The following list gives some indication of the different types of drugs and substances which are used to adulterate the main single substance.

Additives (to bulk out)

Amphetamine: off-white powder, stimulant prescription medicines ground glass, citric acid.

Cannabis: re-pressing good quality mixed with bad quality.

Cocaine: chalk, stimulant-based substance.

Ecstasy: 172 different varieties, any medication which can be made to look like ecstasy. 75mg-225mg in strength.

Heroin: codeine, prescription depressants, brick dust.

LSD: low level of strychnine.

Steroids: human hormone.

Mixes

- Cigarette laced with cocaine or crack.

- Cigarette laced with cocaine and heroin ('Flamethrower').

- Crack or marijuana laced with embalming fluid ('Fry').

- Hashish mixed with opium ('Black Russian').

- Heroin/cocaine   } 'Speedballs'.
- Heroin/amphetamine }

- Heroin mixed with powdered milk ('Cut-Deck').

- Heroin, cocaine, marijuana mixed with various chemicals ('Dust').

- High grade marijuana joint filled with crack ('Buda').

- Marijuana cigarette laced with some form of narcotic ('Amp Joint').

- Marijuana mixed with honey ('Black Mote').

- Marijuana mixed with insecticide ('Fuel').

- Two layers of cocaine with heroin in the middle ('Sandwich').

These are just some of the drug mixes which are being sold or experimented with. There are endless combinations, all of which add to the dangers which drug users can find themselves in if they decide to dabble in drug mixes. If drugs have to be used at all, it would be best to stick to single, relatively safe products – as far as possible.

6

Drug Slang

For those uninitiated into the language of drugs, it can be very confusing and difficult to comprehend all the various meanings of such slang. As in other social pursuits, street drugs have their own particular jargon which not only differs from district to district but also changes in different areas up and down the country.

In particular, drug slang has been developed by both drug suppliers and users mainly to camouflage the real terminology and in order to confuse or exclude those not immediately involved in the drug scene. Street slang tends to be deliberately obscure as, for example: 'dropping love doves' (taking ecstasy tablets) or 'cranking smack' (heroin injecting). Adjoining post code regions are found to have completely different slang terms for the same drug. Gangs or other closed user groups may also be responsible for the remarkable diversity of terms.

The main aim is to keep the communication channels open amongst the drug users without outsiders getting to know what the 'street' is doing. Of course, it may well be that some slang terms stick whilst others only last a very short period before being altered.

Those who first enter into the world of drug taking can often become confused about slang terminology, which will then lead to users making mistakes. The term 'trip', which is most often used to describe the experiences and effects of taking LSD, can be mistakenly applied to the use of ecstasy or amphetamines, for instance. Wrongful application of this term can confuse its meaning.

Drug slang not only refers to the various drugs themselves but also to descriptive terms relating to drug activities. These again vary. Some have been introduced from other countries, especially the USA, which are then adopted in the UK. The following lists have been compiled from research carried out via reliable sources.

Common names of street drugs

Alkyl Nitrites
Ames
Amys
Angels
Bananas
Bolt
Buds
Kix
Liquid Gold
Nitro
Pearls
Ram
Poppers
Rock-Hard
Rush
Snappers
Thrust
TNT

Amphetamines
A1

Amphets
Beans
Billy
Billy Whizz
Black Mollies
Bombido
Bombita
Bumble Bees
Businessman's Trip
Cartwheels
Chalk
Chicken Powder
Chris
Christmas Trees
Co-pilots
Crank
Crossroads
Crystal
Crystal Meth
Diet Pills
Double Cross
Eye Openers
Fast
Footballs
French Blues
Glass
Go
Greenies
Halloo-wach
Hearts
Ice
Lightning
Macka
Meth
Miniberries
Peaches

Pep Pills
Poor Man's Cocaine
Pulver
Red Devils
Rock Crank
Roses
Speed
Splash
Sulph
Sulphates
Thrusters
Toffee Whizz
Truck Drivers
Turnabouts
Uppers
Ups
Wake-amine
Wake ups
Whites
Whizz

Anabolic Steroids

Within this group, most users refer to the trade names of the various preparations:

Anavar
Danocrine
Deca-Durabolin
Delatestryl
Depo-Testosterone
Dianabol
Drolban
Durabolin
Halotestin
Maxibolin
Metandren

Methosarb
Primobolan
Stanazolol
Sustanon 250
Teslac
Testex
Winstrol

Barbiturates

Abbots
Barbies
Barbs
Blockbusters
Blockers
Blue Angel
Blue Bands
Blue Bullets
Blue Devils
Blue Dolls
Candy
Christmas Trees
Downers
F-40s
Goofballs
Gorilla pills
Green Dragons
Idiot Pills
King Kong Pills
Marshmallow
Mexican Reds
Mother's Little Helper
Neb
Nimby
Peanuts
Pink Ladies

Red Devils
Sleepers
Softballs
Stumblers
Yellows

Benzodiazepines

(including chlordiazepoxide (Librium), diazepam (Valium), lorazepam (Ativan), nitrazepam (Mogadon) and temazepam (Normison))

Benzos
Eggs
Jellies
Mazzies
Moggies
Tamazies
Temmies
Tranx

Cannabis

Acapulco Gold
Afghan (black)
Bar
Bhang
Blaw
Blow
Black
Black rock
Boo
Brick
Buddha Grass
Bush
Charas
Charge

Chitari
Cung
Dagga
Dirty
Dope
Draw
Dry High
Dubbe
Fingers
Ganja
Giggle weed
Grass
Griffo
Hash
Hashish
Hash oil
Hay
Hemp
Herb
Ho
Indian hemp
Jane
Joint (the cigarette smoked)
Kajees
Kief
Kif
Lebanese Gold
Loco weed
Marijuana
Malawi Grass
Mary (Mary-Jane)
Mexican Green
Mezz
Mohasky
Moragrifa
Moroccan

Mutah
Nepalese
Olja
One
Panama
Pot
Puff
Quarter Moon
Red Seal
Reefer (the cigarette smoked)
Resin
Rocky
Rope
Sativa
Sensi
Shit
Smoke
Soles
Spliff (the cigarette smoked)
Sticks
Stuff
T
Takrouri
Tea
Temple balls
Thai Sticks
Wacky-bacccie
Wash
Weed
Yesca
Zani

Cocaine & Crack
Base
Baseball

Bernice
Big C
Black Rock
'C'
Candy
Carrie
Cecil
Cha
Charlie
Charlie Coke
Charlie Girl
Cholly
Cloud 9
Coke
Corine
Crack
Crank
Dust
Eight Balls
Flake
Freebase
Freeze
Girl
Gold Dust
Gold Star
Hand Ball
Happy Dust
Ice
Joy Powder
Lady
Leaf
Lido
Loppy Dust
Nose Candy
Paradise
Rock

Roxanne
Royalty
Serpico
Sleigh-ride
Smack
Snow
Snowtoke
Stardust
Stone
Supercloud
Superwhite
Toot
Tornado
Wash
White Cloud
White Girl
White Stuff

Ecstasy

Adam
Big Brown Ones
Burgers
Dennis the Menace
Disco Biscuits
Disco Burger
Doves
E
Eccies
Ecstasy
Ekies
Fantasy
Grey Biscuits
Hamburgers
Hug Drug
Love Doves

M25
Meth Amps
New Yorkers
Orbit
Phase 4
Pink Studs
Rhubarb and Custard
White Doves
Whizz Bombs
XTC
Yellow Callies

Gammahydroxybutyrate

Gamma-OH
GBH
GHB
Liquid E
Liquid X

Hallucinogenic Mushrooms

Magic Mushrooms
Mushies
'Rooms
Shrooms

Heroin

Antifreeze
Big Harry
Brown Sugar
Chasing the Dragon (Smoking)
Chi
Chinese 'H'
Dragon

Elephant
Gear
'H'
Harry
Homebake
Horse
Jack
Junk
Mexican Brown
Poison
Powder
Scag
Scat
Smack
Stuff
Tango & Cash
Thing
Tiger
White Dynamite

Lysergic Acid Diethylamide (LSD)
Acid
Acid Cap
Big D
Blotters
Blue Star
Californian Sunshine
Dots
LSD
Lucy
Mellow
Microdots
Paper Mushrooms
Smiley
Sugar

Tabs
Trips
Window Panes

Solvents
Glue
Gas
Trade Names Of Substances Containing Solvents

Common names of drug mixes

Amp joint	Marijuana cigarette laced with some form of narcotic
Backbreaker	LSD and strychnine
Black mote	Marijuana mixed with honey
Black Russian	Hashish mixed with opium
Buda	High grade marijuana joint filled with crack
Cut-deck	Cigarette laced with cocaine or crack heroin mixed with powdered milk
Dust	Heroin; cocaine; marijuana mixed with various chemicals
Flamethrowers	Cigarette laced with cocaine and heroin
Fry	Crack or marijuana laced with embalming fluid
Fuel	Marijuana mixed with insecticides
Speed ball	Heroin and cocaine or amphetamine
Snow seals	Cocaine and amphetamine

Slang expressions

Ace	Cannabis cigarette
Acid head	Regular user of LSD

Anything going on?	Do you have drugs for sale?
Artillery	Equipment for injecting Drugs
Baby habit	Occasional use of drugs
Back to back	Smoking crack after injecting heroin or heroin used after smoking crack
Backup	Prepare vein for injection
Bad bundle	Inferior quality heroin
Bad go	Bad reaction to a drug
Bad trip	A bad LSD trip
Bag	Drug container
Bag man	Drug supplier
Baller	One who sells a variety of drugs
Balloon	Heroin supplier
Bang	Drug injecting
Banger	Hypodermic needle
Banging	Under the influence of drugs
Barb freak	Barbiturate user
Beat	To do someone out of drugs or money
Beat artist	To inject a drug; inhalant; person selling bogus drugs
Behind the scale	To weigh and sell cocaine
Bent	Addicted
Big John	The police
Big man	Supplier
Bindle	Small bundle of drug powder; heroin
Bing	Enough of a drug for one injection
Bingers	Crack addicts
Biz	Paraphernalia for injecting
Blanks	Poor quality drugs
Blasted	Under the influence of drugs
Blow a stick	To smoke cannabis
Boost and shoot	Steal to support a habit
Booted/buzzing/charged/coasting/flying	Under the influence of drugs
Bridge up/bring up	Ready a vein for injection
Buff	Money

Bull	Policeman
Bummer	Bad LSD trip
Burnout	Heavy abuse of drugs
Business	Paraphernalia for injecting
Bust	Police arrest
Candy man	Drug supplier
Canned	Arrested
Cap up	Transfer bulk form drugs to capsules
Catch up	Withdrawal from drugs
Charged up	Under the influence of drugs
Chasing (the dragon)	Smoking heroin
Chinese eyed	When the eyes become slanted from the influence of marijuana
Choker	Large or powerful hit of crack cocaine
Cleared up	Withdrawn from drugs
Clocking paper	Profits from selling drugs
Coasting	Under the influence of drugs
Cocaine blues	Depression after extended cocaine use
Cocktail	Cigarette laced with cocaine or crack
Cocoa puff	To smoke cocaine and marijuana
Coke bar	Bar where cocaine is openly used
Coked up	Under the influence of drugs
Cold turkey	Sudden withdrawal from drugs
Connect	Buy drugs (from a connection)
Cook up	Preparing for an injection
Crack gallery	Place where crack is bought and sold
Cranking up	To inject a drug
Croaker	Doctor
Croaker joint	Hospital
Cushion	Vein into which a drug is injected
Cut	Mixing drug with a substance to increase bulk
DDU	Drug dependency unit
Deck	A small drug packet
Dibble	Police
Dope	Heroin; marijuana; any other drug

Dropped	Arrested
DS	Drug Squad
Dummy	Poor quality drugs
Easy score	Obtaining drugs easily
Explorers club	Group of LSD users
Factory	Place where drugs are packaged, diluted or manufactured
Fall	Be arrested
Fink	Informant
Fixed	Under the influence of drugs
Flamethrower	Cigarette laced with cocaine and heroin
Flea powder	Poor quality drugs
Fold up	Withdraw from drugs
Following that cloud	Searching for drugs
Garbage	Inferior quality drugs
Gear	Drugs
Gimmicks	Injection equipment
Gluey	Person who sniffs glue
Good go	Proper amount of drugs for the money paid
Groove	Having a good time on drugs
Gun	Equipment for injecting
Gutter junkie	Addict who relies on others to obtain drugs
Habit	Which drug a user is taking
Hand-to-hand	Direct delivery and payment
Hang up	Withdrawal from drugs
High	Under the influence of drugs
Hit	To buy drugs
Hit	Injection
Holding	The effect drug users feel when using drugs – high possessing drugs
Honeymoon	Early stages of drug use before addiction or dependency develops
Hooked	Addicted
Hotload/Hot shot	Lethal overdose
Huffing	Misusing solvent
Hustle	Attempt to obtain drug customers

Icecream habit	Rare drug use
Jab	Drug injection
Jack up	Inject drugs
Jolt	Inject into veins
Joyride	Going out and getting high
Jugged	Arrested
Juggle	Addict financing habit by selling drugs
Junkie	Addict
Kick	Getting off a drug habit
Kit	Equipment for drug taking
Lemon/Lemonade	Poor quality drugs
Lit up	Under the influence of drugs
Machinery	Equipment for injecting
Mainline	Intravenous injections
Make the turn	Withdraw from drugs
Man	Dealer
Meet	Meeting between user & dealer
Monkey on back	Be addicted
Mule	Someone smuggling drugs on their person
Nailed	Be arrested
Necking	Swallowing drugs to avoid arrest
Off your face	High on drugs
On ice	In prison
On the bricks	Released from prison
On the nod	Under the influence of drugs
Outfit	Equipment or paraphernalia
Over and under	Combination of stimulant & depressant
Panic	Shortage of drugs
Paper	Prescription
Pass	Exchange of money or drugs
Percy	Small quantity of drugs for personal use
Piece	Drug container (also gun)
Pillhead	Amphetamine user
Pinned	Constricted pupils whilst on heroin
Plant	Hiding place for drugs
Pop	Injecting

Popping pills	Swallowing drugs
Pusher	Drug seller
Quarter	Quarter of an ounce
Rat	Someone who turns drug dealers in to the police
Reader	Prescription
Roach	Rolled card inserted as air filter in cannabis cigarette (joint)
Rumble	Police investigation
Runners	People who sell drugs for others
Score	Buy drugs
Scratch	Money
Script	Prescription
Sharps	Needles
Stash	Place to hide drugs
Steerer	Person who directs customers to spots for buying crack
Tracks	Row of needle marks on a person
Travel agent	Street drug dealer
Turkey	Poor quality or even non-drug substance
Turned off	Withdrawn from drugs
Turned on	Under the influence of drugs
Wallpaper	Money
Washed up	Withdrawn from drugs
Washing	Preparation for crack cocaine
Wasted	Under the influence of drugs
Weekend habit	Irregular habit
Wired to the moon	High on drugs
Works	Injection apparatus
Wrap	Folded paper packet of drugs
Wrecked	High on drugs
Zonked/Zoinked	Intoxicated on drugs to the point of uselessness

131

Common symptoms of drug misuse	
Symptom	**Likely drug**
Relaxed Sedated Drowsy	Alcohol, barbiturates, benzodiazepines, cannabis, GHB, heroin, opium, solvents
Unconscious	Almost any drug if taken in overdose
Disorientated Hallucinations Distorted perception	Cannabis (high doses), ecstasy, LSD, magic mushrooms, solvents
Excitable Restless Agitated Panic Insomnia	Amphetamines, cannabis, cocaine, ecstasy, LSD Also: Withdrawal from heroin

Figure 7.

7

Signs and Symptoms

Drugs are taken using various ingenious methods. Their intensity and speed of reaction depends very much on the route through which the drug is absorbed. As we have seen, the misuse of drugs can create adverse reactions which could present physiological and non-physiological signs and symptoms or, indeed both.

Substances cause a chemical reaction within the body to produce a number of desired and undesirable effects. The brain interprets a number of physiological and non-physiological responses to the substances. The wealth of material available in today's market has the ability to stimulate or depress the body's natural reactions, which include the brain, in a wide variety of ways.

Secondly, the drug may change physical responses in the body's organs and tissues. The brain then recognises these changes as abnormal symptoms. As a result of continued changes in physical sensations, together with the effects which drugs have on the mind, behavioural changes will take place. Drugs can therefore result in psychological and physiological symptoms.

This chapter addresses the signs and symptoms that are apparent in both physiological and non-physiological drug reactions.

Physical symptoms (in alphabetical order)

Aggression. Alcohol, cocaine and amphetamines may all cause the user to become aggressive, although it is largely dependent on the personality of the user. Long-term misuse of anabolic steroids can cause aggressive behaviour.

Bleeding may be caused when intravenous users are careless during injecting. An internal bleeding process following disruption of the bleeding control mechanisms has been reported in some deaths associated with ecstasy misuse. Bleeding will also result from accidental injuries sustained in falls, from tongue-biting in fits or from violent episodes.

Breathing difficulties may arise from irritation, either in the upper airways at the back of the throat or in the lungs. Choking can occur when there is interference at the back of the throat with the passage of air into the lungs. Suffocation may eventually follow, if a clear airway is not established. If aerosols are sprayed directly into the back of the throat during solvent misuse, the immediate cold may cause spasms of the muscles around the entrance to the windpipe. Choking and eventually suffocation can occur. Suffocation may also result if vomitus is trapped at the back of the throat. Any drug which is inhaled or smoked can cause direct irritation in the windpipe and in the delicate air sacs or the lungs themselves. Smoking cannabis or heroin can cause this. Drugs can directly depress the control of breathing in the centres within the brain. Breathing is 'switched off'. Heroin, barbiturates, benzodiazepines can all cause this.

Convulsions and fits occur when drugs directly overstimulate the brain tissue itself. Convulsions might also occur if the internal environment of the brain is upset, as in cases of heat stroke. Fevers from infections at injection sites and due to septicaemia, hepatitis or HIV may all cause convulsions known as febrile convulsions.

Disorientation in time or in place, sometimes accompanied by confusion, occurs mainly with the psychoactive drugs such as LSD,

134

ecstasy and high doses of cannabis, and with barbiturates and benzo-diazepines. In severe cases, people will experience **hallucinations** which may take the form of seeing things which are not there, hearing, feeling, tasting or even smelling things which are not actually there.

Drowsiness is bought about directly by those drugs that depress the overall alertness of the brain. Typically barbiturates, opiates and ben-zodiazepines can all cause drowsiness in this way. With increased doses, unconsciousness may follow.

Excitability caused by these drugs can also result when there is over-stimulation by use of amphetamines and ecstasy. Insomnia is a clas-sic problem associated with drug users taking amphetamines. It is also a classic feature of heroin withdrawal.

Fainting occurs if not enough blood and hence oxygen reaches the brain. The person will have a slow pulse, be pale with cold skin. Fainting is nature's way of lowering the head so that gravity can assist in increasing blood supply to the brain.

General fatigue follows physical exhaustion and occurs when some-one is coming down from a very active rave under the influence of ecstasy, or after a run of amphetamine use.

Headaches have numerous causes and are common during and after many drug experiences. 'Poppers' are potent at causing headaches because of their effect of sudden dilatation of the blood vessels lead-ing to the head. This is a similar mechanism to the headaches of migraine.

Heat stroke and dehydration, more often occurs because a drug experience causes a sense of abounding energy and excitation. The user, whilst under the influence of the drug ignores, or is not even aware of the warning signs of dehydration, where excessive body fluids, salts and minerals have been lost, mainly through perspira-tion. Amphetamines and ecstasy misuse allow this to occur. The temperature regulating mechanisms of the body fail and the body temperature rises. This is potentially fatal. Alcohol can cause dehydration, because it affects the kidney regulating systems and excessive amounts of fluid are lost in this way.

Hyperventilation or overbreathing upsets the balance of gasses carried within the blood stream and causes tingling and dizziness. Stimulant drugs like ecstasy and amphetamines, commonly cause hyperventilation.

Liver damage. People become jaundiced, with a yellow tinge to the skin and whites of the eyes when the liver is unable to cope metabolising some of the normal chemicals within our bodies. Many drugs damage the liver cells and jaundice is one of the many signs that follow. Excess consumption of alcohol over time causes liver damage (cirrhosis). Hepatitis infection following needle sharing will also cause liver failure and jaundice.

Memory loss has been reported with long term misuse of benzodiazepines and cannabis. Confusion and disorientation can present as short-lived memory loss, while bingeing alcoholics often suffer memory 'blackouts' covering several days which may be permanent.

Muscle cramps, when muscles contract into spasms, occur if the nerves leading to the muscles are over stimulated or if the muscles are not receiving enough blood supply. Peculiar in the first minutes under ecstasy is the cramp or tightening of the chewing muscles of the jaw. Muscle cramps occur during opiate withdrawal and under the influence of cocaine or amphetamines.

Nausea and vomiting are common side effects of many medicinal drugs. It is not surprising that many street drugs produce this effect. First time experience with opiate use is perhaps one of the most potent causes of nausea and vomiting. Almost all drugs can cause dizziness. Dizziness may also directly result from the action of drugs on the balance centres within the inner ear.

Panic reactions. Users will often become hysterical or suffer real panic if they have experienced an abnormal, physical, or psychological event whilst under the influence of drugs. Drugs which directly distort the senses, such as LSD, hallucinogenic mushrooms and high doses of cannabis, can all cause hysteria and panic.

Paranoia, with delusions and suspiciousness of others occurs with stimulant misuse such as amphetamine or cocaine. Some people may become aggressive under the influence of drugs as a result of lifting of inhibitions, or even fearful experiences.

Strokes or cerebrovascular accidents occur when circulation of blood through the delicate vessels within the brain is disrupted either due to haemorrhage or clotting within those vessels. The potent metabolic effects of anabolic steroids may makes their users prone to strokes.

Unconsciousness may be caused by fundamental changes in the body's internal environment, with subsequent effect on brain function. This may be because of dehydration, complete metabolic upset, or because oxygen is not reaching the brain. Any drug which causes deterioration of respiration or circulation of blood can cause unconsciousness in this way. Typically barbiturates, opiates and benzodiazepines are responsible. **Coma** occurs when the person becomes deeply unconscious and cannot be roused in any way.

Non-physical symptoms

Attitude and behavioural changes will rapidly occur once drugs become the all-important, everyday necessities in the life of an individual. Normal activities, such as punctuality, both at work and at school, will become of secondary importance, since the individual will be much more concerned with making sure that the drug supply is readily available.

The uppermost essential priority in the drug misuser's daily existence is the constant recourse to enough funds to feed the drug habit, at whatever cost to family, work and personal necessities. This can deprive the drug misuser of their direction in life, with no definite goals to strive for beyond ensuring that their craving is satisfied. It can also lead to the user adopting criminal behaviour, or 'dropping out' of normal society altogether.

Plans for future targets and advancement, both at work or at school/college or university will be forgotten – family and personal relationships destroyed. Nothing appears more important than the use of the drugs.

Behavioural changes

Both work and school attendance will suffer. A common day for absenteeism is Monday. Weekend drug use, particularly of the stimulant variety which is often followed by depressants to allow the energy level to drop, can be a good reason to stay away, or call in sick.

If the drug supply has become low or been used up, there will be a compulsion to go out and replenish the stock.

The quality of the abuser's work output will quickly deteriorate, perhaps through frequent trips into storage rooms, rest rooms or basements in order to indulge in further drug use such as solvent sniffing or injecting.

Young drug abusers will attempt to lock or hide themselves away from prying eyes at school in order to practise the drug habit. This will show in a marked drop in their educational grades and quality of work. Discipline will certainly be ignored and mood changes can become quite frequent.

Attitudes to driving will undergo a marked change. If the person drives while under the influence, the possibility of road accidents is increased. This shows as a distinct withdrawal from responsibility towards others, ignoring road users, passengers or personal safety.

Mothers who are drug misusers and have responsibility for children will often be incapable of looking after them adequately. The children will then be neglected and often left alone while their mother makes frequent trips in her search for more drug supplies.

Funding and obtaining constant supplies of money will be uppermost in the user's mind. This often becomes an almost insurmountable problem. Money will be borrowed from colleagues at work or from friends.Once this source of supply dries up, more drastic measures will have to be employed and the user will be forced to steal money or items from employers or from home which can then be sold.

Youngsters will look for funding amongst friends, steal from parents or teachers or help themselves to any saleable item from home or in the local shopping areas. Those provided with plentiful pocket money or wages from part-time work who start complaining of having no money should be carefully questioned and other signs of possible drug misuse watched for.

Personality changes

The drug user will develop secretive behaviour related to his/her actions. This may include absences from the work station, with noticeable anxiety in case these trips are causing suspicion among managers and colleagues.

With the younger generation, forged ID cards may appear in their possession, enabling them to frequent places where their age may be questioned.

This age group will also be very aware that police intervention could happen at any time, either by being caught possessing substances or stealing goods from shops or shoppers. Secretive behaviour will be that much more common.

Feelings of responsibility towards the family, such as taking care of them and maintaining a close family unit, will become of secondary importance since this aspect of life is no longer valued.

The drug misuser will often present unusual flare-ups or outbreaks of temper. Drug reactions frequently encourage loss of control, particularly of the emotions and behaviour. Mood changes will become very prominent, such as high elation followed by depression. This may be due to a total loss of direction, or relationships with family or close friends which are no longer functioning effectively or have totally broken down.

139

Periods of depression will occur in the aftermath of stimulant use which then necessitates the need to continue taking the drug to overcome the feeling of depression.

Constant drug misuse will produce poor concentration, causing the drug user to become forgetful, thus being unable to remain on any one subject or task for more than very short periods. This particular state will tend to induce the person to withdraw from taking responsibilities, such as taking control of his/her life or for family and their job. In the case of young women users, especially, there may be an unusual but apparently unshakable relationship with an entirely 'unsuitable' lover, who may indeed be suspected of being her supplier.

The drug user who is in a depressive state will experience strong feelings of insecurity arising from the circumstances the person finds him/herself in; i.e., is there enough money available for the next 'fix'? If not, where is it coming from? Am I going to be found out? and, for those still in employment: if I am caught, will I still have a job? Yet another worry is the often inevitable encounter with the police which can, of course have far reaching consequences.

Social changes

As the addiction continues, the drug misuser will gradually drop his/her usual circle of friends and begin to associate with other known substance users. The new group may well be able to supply the necessary drugs or have access to them. Feelings of guilt or personal blame will be minimised, since everyone within this group is tarnished with the same brush, and moral and financial support are more or less assured.

Normal social activities such as family outings to theatres or cinemas and meals outside the home tend to be disregarded or refused. The drug user will resent having to spend money or time on such endeavours.

Physical changes

People who have lost direction in life through drug misuse will become so utterly concerned with their habit that their physical appearance takes secondary importance. Clothes will no longer look smart or clean, in fact it is of no particular concern or interest what is worn, despite attempts by family members to care for garments or encourage pride in appearance.

Men may ignore the need to shave, since, to them it will be much more important to go in search of new supplies. Women will not be bothered with make-up or hair grooming. Often, washing, showering or bathing and physical hygiene will receive little attention.

If one were to examine the contents of drug users' pockets, one might find collections of paraphernalia, such as tin foil, needles, small spoons, mirrors, razor blades, straws, small bags or paper wraps to contain drugs, all of which would be required and used when the person needs another 'fix'. These 'tools' will be strongly and secretively guarded since they are a tremendous give-away regarding the purpose for which they are being used.

Youngsters will very likely hide the gear somewhere in their room but may not be quite so meticulous in the choice of hiding places.

People who frequently inject may insist on wearing long-sleeved garments despite high temperatures in order to attempt to hide possible injection sites on arms.

Sunglasses are also worn perpetually, often even in dull light, in order to cover up dilated pupils which, again, could be a positive sign of drug misuse.

The drug user will certainly become much more accident prone. They may have frequent falls through loss of balance, and bump into things which will cause bruising. This will be another reason why limbs are covered up – in order to conceal the evidence.

8

Remedies and Assistance

Drug misuse, as we have read, can often lead to the user developing adverse reactions. In order to deal effectively with anyone who may have produced problems, it will pay great dividends to understand and recognise some of the signs and symptoms presented from excess drug taking. Knowing what to do in an emergency may well be instrumental in saving someone's life by quick intervention and basic knowledge of First Aid.

The following list will address the specific implications of the more extreme signs, symptoms and conditions presented by drug abusers.

Above all, when going to the aid of drug misusers, do not put your own safety at risk, for instance by trying to take away hypodermic needles or by intervening where the user is suffering a violent psychotic episode and may be armed. If in doubt, call the police.

Aggression

This can be caused by using alcohol and cocaine and has also been known with bad LSD trips. Steroids, too, will increase the tendency to aggression.

- If it is safe to do so, remove the person from crowded, noisy places and bright lights and talk calmly to them. Needless to say, aggression can turn to violence so be aware of the fact that your own safety may be at risk.

- It often helps to involve the police who are very experienced at dealing with such cases.

Bleeding (heavy)

If a user has attempted to inject into an artery and has caused the vessel to puncture, heavy bleeding with possible spurting of blood will take place. This requires immediate intervention.

- With the aid of any available dressing, press down on the puncture site, applying pressure.

- Immediately raise the limb but retain pressure. Place further pads onto the site but refrain from removing previous pads.

- If bleeding continues, it is futile to continue placing more and more dressings onto the site. In order to avoid serious blood loss, the use of a pressure point near the bleeding point should be used. In the case of bleeding from the forearm, the pressure point would be on the inside of the upper arm between the swatch of muscles. If you have difficulties in locating this point, use the artery in the crease of the elbow joint where blood pressure is normally taken. Press down for ten minutes and then release for a short time, re-applying for a further few minutes until help arrives.

- An ambulance must be called immediately.

Bleeding (superficial)

From cuts, nose or mouth, due to accidental injury. Clean wound and
apply dressing. Patient is possibly in a heightened state of awareness
and may react hysterically to bleeding.

Breathing difficulties

May be due to using crack, depressants or solvents.

- Provided the person is not unconscious, put them in a semi-prone
  position and make sure the airway is clear; if necessary tilt the person's head back.

- Make sure there is no restrictive clothing anywhere, particularly
  round the neck (tight collar or tie).

- Monitor breathing and be prepared to resuscitate . Call for medical
  assistance or an ambulance.

Choking

This condition may be caused through use of solvent spray or vomiting.

- For treatment of vomiting, see relevant section.

- If someone chokes after using solvent spray, clear the airway by
  tilting the head back and removing any objects found at the back
  of the throat (sweeping fingers).

- If the obstruction persists, bend the person forward and give five
  sharp back slaps between the shoulder blades with the flat of the
  hand.

- If this method fails to re-enable breathing, place yourself behind the person and put both your arms round him/her. Clasp your hands together and place them between the belly button and just below the centre rib cage. Thrust inwards and upwards sharply four or five times. Repeat these two procedures until the obstruction clears.

- Should the person become unconscious, straddle them and proceed with horizontal abdominal thrust.

Coma

Can be caused by alcohol, heroin, tranquillisers, poppers and solvents. If overheating takes place from ecstasy or amphetamines, the person can also slip into a coma. There will be no response to any stimulus and the person will be in a very deep state of unconsciousness.

- Make sure the airway is open and the person is breathing.

- Put them into the recovery position, monitoring frequently while waiting for the ambulance, whose crew should be made aware of the person's condition. Be prepared to commence CPR.

Confusion

Caused by taking alcohol, psychoactives, cannabis and barbiturates.

- This condition can be very frightening to people and they therefore need a lot of reassurance and a watchful eye.

- It may be necessary to obtain further medical help. Stay with the person until help arrives.

Cramp

The use of ecstasy, amphetamines, cocaine and opiate withdrawal will produce this symptom. One of the main parts of the body affected when using ecstasy is the jaw muscles. The aim of treating cramp is to help relieve the muscle spasm which is often caused through loss of salt and fluid through severe sweating.

Cramp in the foot:

• Ask the person to stand and put his/her weight on the front of the toes. When relief is felt, massage the foot.

Cramp in the calf:

• Keeping the knee straight, draw the foot firmly upwards towards the shin. Massage the muscles.

Cramp in the thigh:

• Raise the straightened leg and knee. For frontal thigh cramp, bend the knee. Always massage affected muscles.

Disorientation

The main drugs causing this condition are cannabis, LSD and ecstasy. To a lesser extent, drugs like magic mushrooms and alcohol can also be responsible for causing disorientation.

• The person will need to receive more qualified attention, so medical help will be required.

• Never leave the person alone and talk to them in quiet, reassuring ways, making sure they do not cause themselves or others damage.

Dizziness

This will occur through use of alcohol, cannabis, tranquillisers and ecstasy.

- Place the person in a comfortable, safe position on the floor, preferably in the recovery position and monitor.

- Make sure the airway is open by tilting the head back. If the condition does not improve, call 999.

Drowsiness

This will occur if the person has used depressants, opiates, opioids, benzodiazepines and solvents.

- Put the person in the recovery position. Keep talking to them so as to prevent them from slipping into unconsciousness.

- Do not put the person into bed as this may have adverse reactions. If the person complains of thirst, give small sips of tepid water.

- Avoid giving coffee.

- Medical assistance or an ambulance will need to be called.

Excitability

A number of different drugs produce this symptom, such as stimulants, hallucinogenics, LSD, mushrooms and ecstasy.

- Calm the person down by moving them to quiet, semi dark surroundings and talk reassuringly to them.

- If they ask for a drink, give them slow sips.

- An ambulance should be called if the condition does not improve. Monitor while waiting since this condition can deteriorate rapidly.

Fainting

Major drug causing this condition is ecstasy but other substances can also produce a faint. The person will show a slow pulse, pale cold skin and possible sweating.

- Place the person on the floor and raise his/her legs above heart level.

- Loosen tight clothing and, if possible, place near fresh air.

- If consciousness is not regained in a short period, an ambulance should be called. Monitor for breathing and pulse and be prepared to resuscitate.

Fever from injection/septicaemia

This is due to a bad 'hit' (injection) from any injectable drug and needle sharing. It brings with it the dangers of Hepatitis B.

- Cool the person down and obtain medical help as soon as possible, since this is a serious condition.

- If the person slips into unconsciousness, place them in the recovery position and monitor.

Fitting/convulsions

This may be an overstimulation reaction to ecstasy and amphetamines.

- Place the person in the recovery position, assure an open airway and call for an ambulance.

- Clear away dangerous objects in case of injury.

- Monitor and be prepared to give CPR.

Hallucinations

People taking LSD, cannabis and alcohol will experience this symptom. It can be very frightening to the person who goes through a 'trip'. It may even produce panic attacks which present if the person tries to leave the safety of the room and ventures outside.

- It is advisable not to have them removed to hospital since this will take them into an unfamiliar environment of noise and unwelcome questions.

Headache

This can develop when using amphetamines, cannabis, ecstasy, acid and poppers.

- Depending on the severity of the headache, make the person comfortable, either in a chair or on a flat surface, bearing in mind that the drug user can develop other, more sinister symptoms.

- A cool compress on the forehead often relieves pain.

- Avoid, if possible bright lights or loud noise and make sure there is plenty of fresh air.

- Watch for vomiting (see relevant part)

- If the pain increases suddenly or other symptoms such as weakness/drowsiness present, you must seek medical assistance. The person will need reassurance.

Heat stroke/dehydration

Main drugs causing this condition are ecstasy, amphetamines and alcohol.

- Remove the person from overheated surroundings, cool them down by sponging with cold water and fanning them.

- Give them cold drinks, i.e. sports drinks in order to replenish the minerals lost through perspiring.

- If the person's condition deteriorates so that they become drowsy or unconscious, call an ambulance and monitor breathing and pulse. Place in the recovery position.

Hyperventilation

This can be experienced by people taking ecstasy. The person will present rapid deep breathing. Also visible may be trembling, dizziness or feeling faint, cramp in hands and feet and tingling in the hands.

- Place the person in a quiet room and talk to him/her firmly but kindly.

- Sit them down comfortably, preferably on the floor.

- Should the symptoms persist, place a paper bag (not plastic) over the mouth and nose and encourage them to re-breathe their own expired air to replace carbon-dioxide.

Hysteria

Often due to taking psychoactive drugs such as LSD and 'magic mushrooms'.

- Calm the person down by talking quietly to them and give plenty of reassurance.

- Explain that the condition will gradually improve. Remove them to a quiet area with no bright lights

- If possible, avoid taking them to hospital unless other adverse conditions present, such as dizziness and vomiting.

Insomnia

This condition can be brought about through heroin withdrawal or amphetamine use.

- Insomnia (sleeplessness) requires medical intervention. The person should be advised to see a doctor.

- Reassure them but impress on them the importance of treatment and expert intervention.

Jaundice

This is a condition which may be caused by the Hepatitis B virus and by drug damage of the liver. The person will present a yellow tinge on the skin and eyes and show great fatigue. Also reacts badly to any alcohol and fatty foods.

- This condition requires medical advice and attention.

Memory loss

This symptom is found in people using cannabis and benzodi-azepines.

- The person should not be left alone if possible since this condition may put them into personal danger.

- Medical help must be obtained since co-ordination and reaction time will be impaired.

- The person may refuse to allow anyone to take them to hospital. However, call the ambulance since their officers are trained to deal with such situations.

- Calm talking to the user will be much more effective and will help to quiet them down. Explain that this condition will lessen in time and assure the person that they are not going mad,

- If the condition worsens and the person becomes unconscious, the recovery position will have to be used and an ambulance called.

Panic attack

The same method as for hysteria should be applied. This condition presents from using ecstasy and amphetamines.

Resuscitation

Should the person stop breathing and there is no pulse, Cardio-Pulmonary Resuscitation must be given in order to maintain life. The person will not only require constant oxygen input into the lungs, but that oxygen must then be pumped around the body in order to reach all the cells.

- Call the ambulance.

- Before starting, remove any possible obstructions from the back of the throat.

- Tilt the head back and pinch the nose with thumb and index finger to prevent air escaping from the nose.

- Place your lips around the person's mouth, ensuring a good seal.

- Give two good ventilations, removing your mouth after the first one to take in further air yourself.

- Feel for a pulse at the person's side of the neck – in line with the Adam's apple – and if absent, give fifteen compressions by placing your clasped hands on the centre of the person's chest, in line with the nipples. This should be done fairly fast, at the rate of approximately one hundred per minute.

- Continue with two further ventilations and alternating fifteen compressions until the ambulance arrives.

- Should the pulse start again but breathing is still absent, continue ventilating by breathing into the person whenever you feel the need to breathe.

- Check the pulse after every ten breaths.

NB – as a First Aider, it is advisable to have in your possession a plastic face mask for your own protection. These can be obtained inexpensively from any chemist and will help to safeguard against any infection.

Stroke

Sometimes caused by alcoholic excess or anabolic steroids. The person may be drifting in and out of consciousness or become deeply unconscious, depending on the degree of the stroke. One side of the body will become paralysed and, if the stroke presents on the left side, speech will be affected.

- This condition requires urgent removal to hospital.

- If the person is unconscious, the recovery position should be used.

- If consciousness is maintained, put them on the floor with raised head and shoulders. The head should be bent to one side and a towel placed onto the shoulder to absorb any loss of saliva.

- No liquid should be given but the person must be carefully monitored in case breathing stops. Immediately start CPR.

Suffocation

The most common drug misuse causing this symptom is the use of solvents or heavy use of depressants, where a person has to make a conscious effort to breathe.

- Remove, as quickly as possible any plastic bags which have been placed over the head.

- Get the person into the fresh air and remove any tight clothing.

- Open the airway by tilting their head back and monitor for pulse and breathing stoppage.

- Call an ambulance if the person does not respond and be ready to administer CPR while waiting for the ambulance.

- If breathing is present, place the person in the recovery position. Reassure if they are conscious.

Wound infection

This condition can occur through any infected injection site, particularly if the needle has been shared.

- Avoid, if possible, direct contact with someone who has an infection at the injection site (wearing gloves when dealing with wounds is vital, particularly if you have any sores or cuts anywhere on your skin).

- There is a very real danger of cross infection which can produce hepatitis or HIV. The infected person must receive urgent medical attention.

- Cover the infected site with a dressing and raise the limb to eliminate any swelling. After treating the person, make sure you wash yourself thoroughly.

Unconsciousness

This condition can result from the taking of any drug, depending on how it affects the user.

- Check breathing and pulse and administer CPR if necessary, Loosen any tight clothing.

- Keep the person warm but avoid this if overheating has taken place.

- Put the person in the recovery position and monitor.

- Call the ambulance, giving details to ambulance control about the incident and your findings. Stay with the person until help arrives.

Vomiting

There are many drugs which can induce vomiting, depending on the person's reactions. Particularly alcohol, solvents and early use of heroin.

- Should the person have become drowsy or unconscious, place them in the recovery position. This will prevent vomitus inhalation which can prove fatal.

- Never induce vomiting in anyone, e.g., by sticking your fingers down their throat, since this can cause further problems.

- Look for any clues which might identify the cause of vomiting, such as a strong smell of alcohol or cans/bags of solvent. Any samples should be sent with the person to hospital which must, unfortunately, include some of the vomitus.

- While waiting for the ambulance, monitor breathing and pulse and keep the person warm.

9

Intervention

Breaking free

The whole issue of drug taking and the development of drug dependency is highly complex and many people become subject to its repercussions in one way or another.

Those engaged in any form of habitual drug misuse can damage themselves as well as creating adverse effects on their family, friends, colleagues at work and, in the long run, on the general community. It should be remembered, too, that drug misusers may render others liable to prosecution: any employer, for instance, is liable if an employee is found in possession of or using illegal drugs whilst in the work premises, whether it is known that the person is a misuser or not. The employer will receive a heavy fine and might even find him/herself forced to attend a Court hearing.

Some drug users may want to curtail their habit or even give it up totally but are very reluctant to take that first step in seeking help. Other groups of users may have become involved with crime, mostly in the form of theft or burglary in order to fund their habit. This can lead to violence if the attempt at supplementing funds fails.

For these reasons, it is important not to lose sight of care and rehabilitation as methods of treating drug misuse.

Any signs that a friend, colleague at work or relative might be heading for a problem will have to be approached with great care. Direct confrontations and challenges will only serve to drive the user into more secretive ways of continuing the habit. Certainly, it may be that the individual will need to undergo an enormous personal journey into the abyss, hitting absolute rock bottom, and perhaps watch companions die, before they can persuade themselves that it is time to seek help.

One of the most important preconditions for a course of action which will eventually lead to a drug-free existence is the ability and willingness of the drug user to admit that a problem has developed. This admission will enable them to put themselves into the hands of professional people who can oversee a detoxification program and eliminate some of the physical withdrawal symptoms which will undoubtedly be experienced. Social support and counselling can then be put in place. Drug-dependent individuals however are most often those who resort to drugs to mask deeper insecurities and avoid facing underlying problems; it is extra hard for such people to realise that what, for them, appears to be the cure for all their ills is really the disease. Denial is the first refuge of the addict.

We have already explored in this book, some of the characteristic behaviour and personality changes that can indicate when a person is starting to use drugs too frequently, and which may throw more light on those suspicions one may have formed. Let's look more closely now at this problem from a personal point of view, bearing in mind that most people, especially youngsters, are nowadays exposed to the temptations of the drug trade and may be tempted to experiment with one substance or another – just to be more like you, perhaps?

• Has the person changed in some unexpected way?

• Is there any sign of decreased general physical well-being?

• Is there a decrease in social activity, signs of withdrawal, problems with keeping on top of work or any other adverse clues that there may be a drug problem?

- If the person has already admitted to using drugs, is there a marked difference in their physical or mental behaviour pattern?

- Do they sometimes admit that they have 'overdone the habit'?

- Do they appear to have money problems?

- Is there any evidence that their drug taking is on the increase, beyond the level of just having tried it?

- Are there any signs that the person may be using injection methods, such as puncture marks on visible parts of the body?

Most people at some stage in their lives need to rely on others, such as friends, colleagues or family for some support, however small the contribution may be. Drug dependent people often feel that society in general looks down upon them, indeed they often have a very negative self-image which they will 'project' on to others: "You perceive me as worthless, so I'm going to prove to you just how worthless I can be, then you'll see I'm really worth something". This attitude can, of course produce suspicion, isolation, insolence and a refusal to co-operate with those who may genuinely wish to give support.

Listening without blame or censure is a first important step towards gaining someone's confidence. If knowledge of help procedures exist, they should be suggested but without labouring the point. Ultimately the decision to seek medical help and counselling will have to be made by the drug user themselves.

An offer to accompany the person to one of the various help agencies, which could include their General Practitioner, a drug support agency, a trained and qualified counsellor or a charity such as ADFAM (see Appendix for list of support agencies), will often give the user the incentive and courage to take that first step.

People at work can often get useful advice from their Personnel Manager who has to adhere strictly to the code of confidentiality. Of course, the fear of losing one's job may often prevent employees from discussing their particular problem with managers. Drug dependence

FACTORS DETERMINING DRUG USE

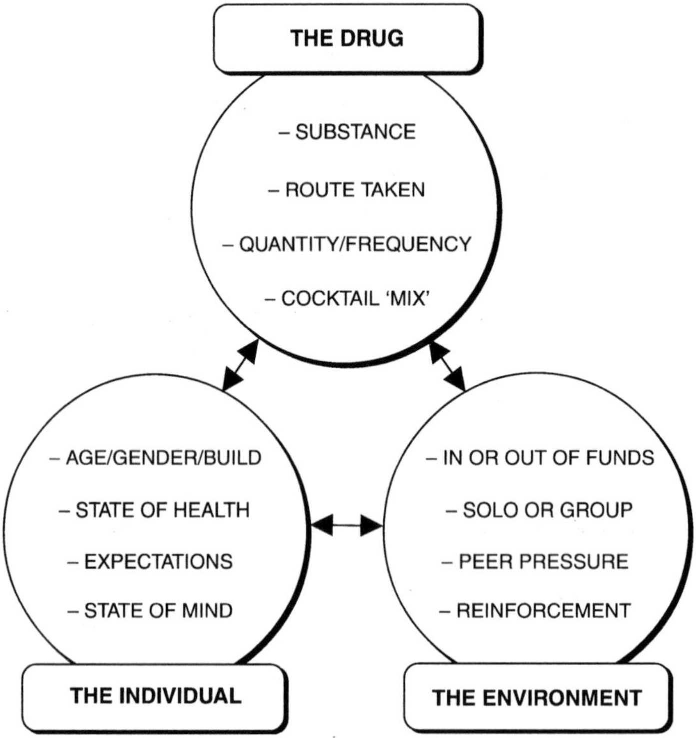

THE DRUG

- SUBSTANCE

- ROUTE TAKEN

- QUANTITY/FREQUENCY

- COCKTAIL 'MIX'

- AGE/GENDER/BUILD

- STATE OF HEALTH

- EXPECTATIONS

- STATE OF MIND

THE INDIVIDUAL

- IN OR OUT OF FUNDS

- SOLO OR GROUP

- PEER PRESSURE

- REINFORCEMENT

THE ENVIRONMENT

Figure 8.

seems to be so much more heinous a crime than the many other forms of addictive or damaging behaviour which your Personnel Officer would be only too glad to help you with.

Lessening the harm

'Harm minimalisation' acknowledges that drug misuse exists and entails policies and programmes aimed at reducing the risks of drugs and drug using to individuals and society. These can range from advice on safer drug use to community action programmes. One important step recently has been the increase by the police in the use of cautions for possessing small amounts of cannabis, as it has been perceived that prosecuting occasional users who are otherwise upright citizens in the courts can create more problems than it solves.

There are many sources where advice and information can be obtained. So, what kind of services are available and what do they offer? Also, what kind of commitment do they expect from the user?

- Drop-in centre. This is a place where people can go for a cup of tea and a chat. These centres provide a non-threatening environment which will be non-judgemental, providing a safe environment. The person will receive honest acceptance and will be given accurate information and maybe introduced to a helper with experience of drug dependency themselves.

- A personal visit. The drug user may not feel capable or able to visit any of the services personally. It may well be possible for someone to come and visit for an informal chat. Also, check to see if the centre welcomes friends and family, so you can provide extra security and support.

- Many organisations have set hours when they are available for consultations. These should be investigated. Another important point to watch for is whether an appointment needs to be arranged or if the user can 'drop in' during hours of business. It is more positive to arrange an appointment since that makes a commitment.

- Confidentiality will be a very important issue to a drug user, especially if it involves questions relating to the law. Although drug agencies must have a code of practice, it is worth the user's while to reassure him/herself on this point. Records may well be kept about the person seeking help and this is also worth checking. Who will have access to these records and how are they stored?

- Drop-in centres are designed to meet the needs of those who seek help. This may include needle exchange for those who inject, provision of detoxification, such as treatment with methodone in order to stabilise heroin dependent people and, above all educational programmes about drugs.

• Some of the helping organisations in any area will be able to give advice and information, either personally or by phone. These include:

a)   Drug advice and counselling services
b)   Services which treat with substitute drugs
c)   General Practitioners
d)   Drug Services offered in Hospitals, either in- or out-patient
e)   Rehabilitation centres, usually residential
f)   Centres for needle exchange
g)   Drug users' self-help groups.

A first enquiry can be made to the Regional Health Information Service on 0800 665544 (toll-free number). Other helpful numbers may be found in the Appendix at the back of the book, in the many regional 'alternative' guides now available, or in Yellow Pages.

A helping hand...

A *positive attitude* towards themselves and about the actions they can take to cure the problems should always be foremost in the minds of those who are willing to lend a helping hand. It is often very difficult to support someone with drug problems, but it should be remembered that it is often extremely difficult for the drug dependent person to make that first move towards a healthy lifestyle. At first, they will be unrewarding patients; ultimately, they will need all your strength and willpower to make it happen.

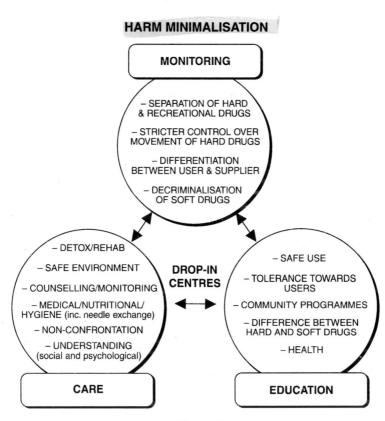

Figure 9.

10

Case Studies

The following case studies are based on real-life cases of alcohol and drug dependant people. In most cases, they have sorted themselves out and are now leading normal lives. As we have shown previously, every drug misuser has an individual story to tell. The aim of including these six examples is to illustrate some of the points we have made in previous chapters, and perhaps to assist the reader with identifying possible problems in their own family and circle of friends; seeing how cases may develop, understanding what the pressures are, and knowing what outcomes may be possible, given proper management.

'Jules'

We are concerned here with a recreational drug user who experimented with and used various types of drugs, mainly for enjoyment, amongst his peer group. Experimentation with some substances only took place once, and the reader will understand how logic and sense prevailed after the first and only trial.

Jules is able to trace back his early interest in drugs and how it developed later.

"I first got the idea of drugs when I was 3-4 years old. I learned to read very early and got hold of some books which described altered states of mind, which gave me an insight into ones abilities to do different things, in particular a truth-type drug. Most of the stories were science fiction and I found them intriguing. I first tried drugs when I was between 16-18 years old, when I started to experiment with different things. It was well thought out – not peer pressure, or because this was what everyone was doing. I now had the chance to try something which had been fascinating me all my life. These were substances which allowed me to say: "Let's see where it leads me."

Jules started his experimentation with marijuana, which was bought and shared within his peer group. All manner of things were sold in order to make some money and it all started before Jules left school.

"The first reaction from our experimentation was somewhat disappointing," he recalls, "as cannabis is a learned drug. I did get a kind of 'high' the first time, but certainly not what I expected. It seemed to be anti-addictive: the more you smoked, the higher you got. It was a little disappointing that I didn't get to all those wonderful places one was supposed to go in one's head, but the whole thing was kind of nice and progressive. Since our expenses were not great, we were able to afford the low cost of the drugs – it was certainly less than spending an evening at a pub." The dose Jules took initially increased as he got more used to the drug. He mentioned that it was important to experiment with the right dosage which was suitable for him. He increased the amount because he enjoyed it and certainly didn't feel any ill effects.

He recalls: "There were a certain number of social/liberal state-
ments to be made. Cannabis meant you were part of the social revolution and this was tremendously important to differentiate US from
THEM. It was an affirmation of the movement we were part of. It was
our symbol and our token."

Jules's main substance was cannabis and he claims that he did not
mix it with alcohol too often since this was not a clever thing to do.
He often smoked in the early morning, not because he was fighting off
a drug hangover but, "to start the day off right". He mentioned that the
effect was immediate. "Just to hold a joint in my hand and sniff it gave
me a reaction. It was not physical or psychological but almost a psychologically instant high." This would last several hours, during
which time the group shared several joints. Then other things were
done until someone would light up another joint. Jules was never concerned about adverse effects through sharing joints since everything
was heated, sterilised and considered to be quite safe.

Jules was never very keen to venture onto other, more potent
drugs. His group experimented with some different substances
because, as he says, "they were there." Occasionally amphetamines
mixed with cannabis were tried – one was an upper, the other a
downer – while very occasionally there would be some opium around
which produced hallucenogenic tendencies. Jules tried LSD just once
and his experience with this drug gave him the following insight:
"Instead of 'hey, that was good, let's do it again, it was: 'that was
really good, thank you."

The following is an account of Jules's LSD trip:

"I bought a small tablet. We all went out for a meal and I had forgotten that I had already taken the tablet. I had ordered pancake which
began looking like an ice cream sundae, rather like a piece of sculp-
ture, the visual captivity of which invited touching and handling. My
hands waved over the top, making conjuror's passes at it. We wan-
dered back to someone's flat, put some records on and the walls of the
room started breathing which gave me a nice, warm comfortable feeling. People were drifting in and out and, at one point I thought I
would like to look at the stars but felt it was safer inside. Various pic-
tures came alive and started to talk to me. One was of Bob Dylan.

Those things which were real in the first place became more real and I felt that I was going through a whole dream state. Surrealist paintings are not far off it – there was a point of increasing religious experience, a sense of something very much greater, something up and above, very warm, light, bright, becoming something inside which I would have thought was a soul or a mind trying to blossom and extend from it. I was getting what I found to be overload on some video cameras. Most of the experiences I had were exaggerations of what was already there. Music which contained scratches put me in mind of a lovely log fire. Then I was in a tropical place and I was experiencing ME from a very young age to adulthood – all at the same time. I knew it was interesting, I don't know if I learned anything from it, but it was important to me to see myself simultaneously during all those years. By now it was getting towards the end of the trip.

"Now that I am reliving this, it seems to me that it was tremendously inward looking. Another person, who was not having a good trip, came in, tore up their cheque book and went out again.

"The whole of my trip was in brilliant colour. There was one slightly bad moment when I was coming out of it. I looked in the mirror and saw a slight cut above my eye. I started hallucinating and saw my face cracking like a piece of glass, with blood oozing out of the corner of my eye. I told myself that this was interesting but it is only a trick. The whole thing took about twelve hours. It was like taking a look at reality in a three dimensional way. For weeks afterwards I was aware that whatever I saw, there was always a little bit more around it."

During this period, Jules was spending quite a small proportion of his earnings on drugs. Everyone lived frugally, so sometimes more would be bought than was needed and sold on to make some money but it was never excessive.

Jules recalls: "Although I shared accommodation with others, they were not necessarily the same group that I shared drugs with. It was fairly fluid. In any group there were one or two who really felt that out there was a new world. There were more who supported this view – I was one of them. This was not because we were all louts but it was a claim for freeing your mind, that you could actually live what you believed in. Most of the others were those hangers-on who hung onto anything."

Jules personally did not take any hard drugs, although the rest of his group experimented with heroin and cocaine sniffing. His view is that cannabis is a relatively harmless substance, certainly no more harmful than alcohol, tobacco, coffee or aspirins, which he classes as a more dangerous drug.

Not many of his group went over the dividing line – and he claims: "Those who did would have gone over anyway. If you are going to be an addict, chances are you'll start with something easy and work up. However, that doesn't mean that everyone will climb that ladder. Alcoholics will start with beer and work up to meth."

Jules found alcoholism much harder to control, in fact he claims that he came much closer to becoming an alcoholic than a drug user. "It was easier to step back from drugs than from alcohol. The only reason I stopped taking marijuana for a long period was because it was not available, so I drifted out of it and never regretted it. Yes, I would like to smoke it from time to time because I enjoy it, but – no regrets. I had much more of a problem cutting down on alcohol and also to stop smoking. Cannabis was much easier and, in any case it is more comfortable not doing something illegal.

Jules was once caught by the police during a raid on the flat; he was the only person there at the time. He was charged but the next day got a conditional discharge. He claims that it certainly did not ruin his life or career. When Jules decided to cut drugs out, it was a gradual stopping because the drug became less available. It was a decrease in the environment, not the drug.

The only time Jules allowed himself to slip was when he mixed cannabis with alcohol, and he recalls being careless: "I used to pay no attention when crossing the road and then pretend that I was drunk or stoned and that it wasn't my fault. One day I caught myself doing it, at which point I realised how stupid I was being and started to take responsibility for my actions again. I made the decision to keep myself together despite what was going on, although I still maintain that it is my responsibility if I want to smoke it or not.

With Jules, lifestyle and health go hand in hand – they are all part of the bohemian scene. He claims never to have been ill through drug taking. He sometimes feels the desire to take drugs again, and in fact, has done so on several occasions during the last few years, but is determined not to let it become a habit again.

His family was not very affected by his drug habit; he claims that they were aware of it but rarely commented. He thinks his mother would have preferred him to drink beer since that contains vitamins! Jules would advise anyone thinking of using hard drugs to resist the temptation. "If they must use anything, then go for cannabis, it is the only drug of the illegal variety I would recommend.

"Talking about drug use, of course it was legally wrong but for my group and countless others it was definitely right. I still maintain even now that it is not morally wrong. Okay, it is not a revolution – as a symbol and badge it is fairly pointless. But I would campaign for the legalisation of softer drugs on the grounds that it is unnecessary to ban them. The law is restrictive and it is a matter of freedom, liberty and free choice, the choice to make the right or wrong decisions." Jules considers that everyone takes responsibility for their own actions, but within the recreational scene most people have a fairly good idea of what they are doing anyway.

As an afterthought, Jules claims: "One thing I have never done is take drugs or alcohol because I was depressed – it wouldn't have worked anyway."

'Mike'

Mike is in his mid-thirties and comes from a family of police officers, his father being a retired high ranking officer with a successful career behind him. Money was never a problem but his values were somewhat Victorian and Mike's upbringing was strict, with both parents being very domineering. His father had a power fixation and was fascinated by people who displayed great dominance over others. Mike's mother was very status conscious, and he recalls great friction in the family. "I have never looked too closely at any possible connection between this and my subsequent drinking, probably because I'm frightened to face it – my father invariably encouraged my drinking, he used to call it being manly."

The family were all heavy drinkers and Mike was frequently taken to pubs on a Sunday before lunch at an early age – 15/16 years. After taking A levels, this drinking increased: "A lot of my friends and I used to get drunk, but I never suffered from hangovers."

As with the immediate family, Mike decided to join the police force and at 18 he moved to London and became a uniformed police officer in Central London. This embraced quite a heavy drinking culture which increased when he moved to CID, attached to Soho, amidst a whole variety of clubs.

"My drinking increased dramatically – mainly through peer pressure and because of the environment in which we worked. Social drinking just went with the job – there was no definitive line that was crossed, most days it simply melted into a day-to-day drinking session", recalls Mike.

Mike and his colleagues frequently met on Fridays to discuss work patterns of the week and then continued their drinking sessions well into the evening and often late into the night. He recalls: "It was never 'I'll have a few bottles of beer and go home'; it became the norm to get drunk and then go home."

Mike had recently got married and even then his wife was saying that she felt he had a problem with drink. His volume of intake at that time was about twenty pints a day, but this was done over a controlled period of time. His work lasted approximately thirteen hours a day, seven days a week. It started at 9am and finished at 10pm, but the drinking carried on until well beyond midnight. Since the job entailed getting to know the people of Soho, drinking with them became part of that job.

Although that phase of Mike's career changed after several years in the CID, his drinking habit, if anything, increased. He became obsessive about it. He felt: "If Jo Bloggs drank twenty pints, I had to drink twenty-two and in our group sessions I was always the one who was one drink ahead of everyone else."

Other people began to notice that the drinking was getting out of hand. Mistakes were made and memory lapses occurred. His wife became more and more disenchanted with his drunken orgies but Mike's response was: "If I'm an alcoholic, so is everyone else."

Although no physical ill effects showed for a good many years, eventually tremors were present on waking up. His whole body shook, after which voices were heard. By this time Mike had been drinking heavily for the best part of twenty years, nineteen of them had produced no bad reactions. Then, within a very short time, sleepless nights, cramps in the leg muscles and feelings of paranoia developed. "Things were coming out of the walls, particularly at night. There were very vivid and horrible hallucinations – reality and hallucinations got mixed up. It became very frightening and I used to dread going to bed. I used to say, 'It can't be the drink, it has never happened before', but then a little voice would say: 'Of course it is the drink, stop it, you are going crazy'."

Mike found that the only thing which would stop these withdrawal symptoms if he resisted the urge to have a drink was to carry on drinking and, although he never actually vomited, he felt physically sick and had difficulty picking up his glass. Once that first drink was taken after the night, he was once more, as he put it, "away again." From then on, Mike went downhill very fast. His job, house, car, and wife and child all went. "Things which took me a lifetime to accumulate went within six months."

Mike was on sick leave for two years, during which time his drinking went from severe to almost the point of oblivion. Towards the end he attempted suicide. Mike recalls: "I wanted to stop – I prayed for something to happen that would make me stop, but I couldn't. I used to openly pray at night for something to happen and my eventual recovery brought about a lot of guilt."

Mike was arrested for drink-driving and lost his licence. About a month after that he once more got behind the wheel despite the fact that there was a ban on his driving. "Something seemed to snap inside me – I started the engine, put my foot on the accelerator and drove straight into a brick wall." Once more Mike was over the limit and this time he was banned for three years and put on probation after a psychiatric report.

The Force were very understanding and gave him premature retirement.

After his 'brick wall' incident, Mike was admitted to a psychiatric ward of the hospital and that was the turning point. During his worst period, Mike had hit rock bottom. He had stopped caring about his appearance, health or people. "Nothing mattered but the drink."

Mike finally realised that his 'habit' had to stop or else it would kill him. Although, for a year, all the help he received from his GP was the advice to 'pull himself together and stop drinking', and no other assistance was offered.

Once Mike left hospital, he joined a group and began a supervised rehabilitation programme which consisted of group discussions, going into aspects of addictive behaviour such as denial, dysfunctional families, self esteem, confidence building and a number of other important therapeutic inputs. Mike recalls: "The first sentence I learnt was, 'No-one is more important than me'." The rehabilitation programme has been very successful and Mike has been dry for well over a year. He claims: "I never felt that I wanted to return to alcohol from the day I woke up in hospital. It took away so much of my life and caused so much heartache. Now, my wife and child have returned and our relationship is much firmer. We talk more and are both more willing to listen.

Mike's final advice to other alcoholics is: "Never think you can cope with the problem on your own. By the time you think that, it is already too late. If you can see that you are losing things through drinking, seek help. After all, it is there for the asking."

'Peter'

Peter's alcohol dependency began when he was seventeen, shortly after his father left home. His mother took him and his brother to Ibiza on holiday, and, as Peter says: "Alcohol at that time wasn't part of my life."

Shortly before returning home, while he was sitting in the hotel lounge, Peter had a very frightening experience. He explains: "Suddenly the whole room went up in the air. I sank into the nearest chair and was absolutely terrified. My mother and brother took me to my room where I went to bed and stayed until we returned home three days later."

It was a panic attack. Peter spent the next nine months housebound, afraid of a repeat of the incident in Ibiza. On his various attempts to go out, he would get no further than five yards up the road, panic and have to return home with a pounding heart.

After nine months without any kind of help, a friend persuaded Peter to join him and a group of friends at a nearby social club. "I had to be dragged there, I was so scared," recalls Peter. At the club he was handed a pint of very strong bitter which calmed him down. After another pint, a trip into the country was suggested and drinking continued during the journey. Peter remembers: "For someone who had been housebound for nine months, I was doing well. I knew nothing about alcoholism at that time, but I realised that I was having one of the most marvellous afternoons of my life – it was total release."

That was the turning point, since Peter felt that he had found the answer to his problem. For the next twelve years he drank, starting at lunchtime, by which time he felt that he really needed it.

During this period, with the help of alcohol, Peter went from strength to strength. Home life, possessions, job and recreational activities, which included world snooker tournaments, were at a peak. In fact, he claims: "Everything I touched turned to gold, and all with the help of drink." Then suddenly, everything went out of control. He sustained a knee injury and, in order to help him get to hospital for physiotherapy, Peter turned to morning drinking for the first time to give him the courage to go out. After that, he says, he could never break the habit. It also took him on a further downward slide. Peter was now drinking at all hours of the day and evening. His employers were supportive and organised medical help and a detoxification programme which included a variety of tests, but he was suspended from his job for six months.

During this period, Peter's wife decided to leave him and, within a very short time, he had lost his job, his house and his wife. Peter said: "That was the very worst time and I actually ended up sleeping in my car."

Peter then had a couple of fits and stopped eating. In order to keep up his strength, he increased his alcohol intake. He recalls: "My weight dropped from 11½ stone to 7 stone within six to seven weeks. The cycle just went on and on, but I still didn't accept that I had become an alcoholic."

Blame for Peter's predicament was placed on anything and everyone. While he was still employed, his boss became the scapegoat. Peter sought help from a support group, which he attended three times in the space of one year, but claims they gave him no real help or encouragement. He remembers: "Every time I left there, I went straight down to the off-licence to buy more drink. I just wouldn't or couldn't accept that I was dying from a terminal illness."

By this time, Peter was living in a bed and breakfast hostel. One morning he woke up and heard a voice say: "You've got to stop now." Terrified, he stayed in bed for the next two days; but, since then, from being a functional, or everyday, alcoholic, he has become a 'binger' instead. He claims: "I can go for five days at a time without a drink, but after that it is back to bingeing."

Peter has recently come out of rehabilitation again, which is a very tough course. He attended for three months, after which he was sent to a follow-on place. Peter confessed: "The train was cancelled and I panicked. My first reaction was to go and have a drink. On my return to rehab I admitted to this and luckily they sorted me out."

Another nineteen weeks were spent at yet another centre, after which, while trying to keep an appointment, he again panicked and had a few drinks to bolster up his courage. Once again, on his return to the centre, he confessed – but this time, the authorities were contacted and

Peter was rejected from the course. Back to square one... He was at least told: "When you are dry, you can come back for more help". He says: " This is easier said than done, when you are terrified of getting out amongst all those people. I manage a week without a drink but after that it will start all over again."

So, if not the drink itself, what is at the core of Peter's problem? He remembers going to the doctor about a year after that first experience of agoraphobia in Ibiza, but this was a waste of time. His explanations about his fear and panic feelings when walking down the road and trying to find a place to hide produced no sympathy or help. Peter recalls: "At that time, I honestly thought I was going mad. All in the space of one and a half years my dad had left home, my brother moved out, the girl I loved moved away from the area and I had to leave England on that holiday. I was petrified."

Much later, during therapy Peter came to realise that all this loss and his having to take on board a premature adult role had simply been too much to cope with. Peter agrees that, although this may have contributed in some way, it is by no means the only reason why he was using alcohol as a drug. He claims: "If you put an alcoholic drink and a pill in front of me, I'll take the pill every time. This worries me since I don't actually like alcohol itself, only the effect of it. I could so easily become a drug addict although so far I've only taken prescribed drugs."

After Peter has been dry for a while, he will have just one drink which then increases the next day to several and before long he is back on the bottle. He says: " The little man sitting on my shoulder says, 'Don't forget me. I saw you through those bad times.' I know I have to tell him to go away but it doesn't always work. Just one drink is the trigger." Once the cycle recurs, Peter can't remember how much he has had; after a good many binges, he wakes up in a police cell. He never becomes violent or gets involved in fights, he just falls into a drunken stupor.

Altogether Peter has had three fits, mainly due to withdrawal symptoms when he has tried coming off alcohol. During one of these fits he re-injured his knee. He has been in hospital three times on a detox programme, which has made him feel very guilty. However, his power of recovery seems to be quite quick and he is able to leave his bed and eat normally again after about three days. Blood tests, to Peter's surprise, tend to show up normal, as his habit of bingeing gives his body time to recover between bouts.

Peter has also twice suffered hallucinations, seeing flies swarming round his feet. He recalls: "I had to persuade myself that they weren't really there."

During attempted drying-out periods, if no medication is available, Peter will stay in bed for two days, during which time he will sweat, shake and vomit. If he attempts to leave his room any sooner he has recurring panic attacks. "It has been suggested that I get counselling, but this frightens me so much; it is fear of the fear and I just can't handle it." Peter is aware that he is suffering from agoraphobia but is, as yet, unable to piece together the reasons behind this.

"I now take each day one at a time", Peter declares. "One drink now would see me back in a police cell. It is really down to me to admit things are not right and then do something about it."

Denial is one of the most natural defences in the life of an alcoholic.

'Russell'

Russ, as he likes to be called, started in the drug scene as a recreational user but somehow got carried away with his experimentation. He is a very determined person and, once he realised that this habit had turned into a very dangerous situation, he did all he could to obtain help. This is his story and, because of the nature of the drug misuse, Russ will relate his experiences in his own words:

"I became involved with drugs at the age of fifteen. I wanted to experience drugs and I tried cannabis and amphetamines, which was basically about it. This was during the last year at school and it continued for quite a few years until I became dependent on opiates. I was a recreational user in a small group. We used ecstasy when I was twenty – this was the dance rave. After that I used opiates on and off and, for the last couple of years I got addicted. I used no other drugs apart from amphetamines and opiates. The last drug I took was a cocktail of methadone, hydrochloride in 50ml ampoules and dexedrine, crushed and injected. That was my special thing. When I was at school, I got the cannabis from people in their 30s and 40s, recommended by relatives and friends. I went to a school with 500 boys and only three of us as far as I knew took drugs at the time of my last year. You have to know people to get the drugs. Not much advice was given at that time. As a young recreational user you are invincible – immortal – and you don't take notice of outside advice. If someone wants to take drugs they would have to be very rational to allow themselves to be persuaded not to do it. You only get a few who end up as statistics in the paper, while for the rest it is a massive culture.

"I started taking drugs for my own experimentation. At that age a lot of teenagers experiment with alcohol, cigarettes and drugs. It didn't ruin my life at all. This is the first time I have been unemployed since leaving school. I had a mortgage, and was going to get married, but this relationship was dissolved, not through opiate use, just friction. It was purely recreational use, either with my group or after coming home at night, watching TV and having a puff. I never smoked cannabis at work as it clouds your mind and I can't operate like that. It makes you very lethargic and you don't want to do any work. I just used it for enjoyment. I used to listen to music and it opened my mind to literature.

"Amphetamines were for the other end of the scale, such as parties and having a good time. I still use amphetamines occasionally but have never become either physically or psychologically dependent. There are a lot of amphetamines on the street – whatever you want. Very few people do become physically or psychologically dependent on amphetamines; it is very rare.The thought of taking amphetamines regularly revolts me, it is a very exhausting drug which can give you great euphoria and great energy and staying power, but it also takes it out of you – you have to sleep, and when you come down the sensation is very nasty. There is always a minus to every plus in this world. To keep taking amphetamines, you have to be a special person. I only know two people who carried on using it into their 40s and 50s and it has had a mental and physical effect on them – they are very muddled.

When I first started with my little group of four or five friends, we were outcast for using drugs amongst our own age group. This is not so evident amongst older people who had used drugs when they were younger. I have always had a burning desire to try drugs but there was no peer pressure. In fact, everyone tells you *not* to take drugs – it is a matter of 'buy your own ticket, take your own life'.

"I got bored with being a recreational drug user so I went onto opiates. I did all the raves, underground parties, weekend parties etc., and got very bored with it all by the time I had reached the age of 28. It is very much youth orientated and you can't do it when you get into your late twenties. You have to go to work and also, you have to sleep to recuperate. I did take temazepam to come down but those drugs were very hard to obtain. Everyone keeps saying that all drugs are easy to come by but they were not. Nowadays it seems to be easier but I don't really know since I'm not in that scene any more.

"Recreational drug taking has no effect on your lifestyle. You can be completely normal. No-one knows you are doing it except the culture you are doing it with. There are thousands of people going to work on a Monday morning, from barristers to bricklayers, who at the weekend get dressed to go out and use drugs, and no-one knows about it. They usually look a lot healthier than those who have been on the beer all weekend. I have used drugs during the week and in particular cannabis all my adult life. I used to get home after work, have a couple of whiskies and a couple of joints to relax me.

"To take any other form of drugs, as I have done, you would have to make a conscious decision and be aware that you would have to pay for the after-effects the next day. It is up to you, whether you want to make the day even harder for yourself.

"If you were out for 24 to 48 hours and not eating, you'd be suffering from exhaustion and dehydration. The worst after-effects I've ever had after long-term use of amphetamines with no food or sleep for three to four days were hallucinations, both audial and visual, plus paranoia; that's why I stopped using amphs. Even with just weekend use after long-term recreational use I'd feel paranoid during the week, which was a most unpleasant experience. You know what it is but can't stop it. You become very self-conscious, aware and worry about everything. A most awe-inspiring black shadow comes over you, which is horrible. I gave up cannabis for the same reason, you suck yourself into an inner world, eventually I couldn't even go into a pub any more.

"If you get nice, clean, strong drugs, you don't have to increase the dose, you are the one who controls the dose. But you have to be sensible with it because if you binge, you'll be out for a very long time. You have to control what you want to get out of it. I lost a lot of weight through physical exhaustion and not eating, but it was mainly a mind game of paranoia.

"Drugs are not really that expensive if you are working and you can always bulk buy for reduced cost which will last that much longer. I've never had a criminal record and have always worked. Car thefts, burglaries, etc., are just not my scene, I don't know anything about it. I've always been able to pay for my drugs. Also, I like to know what I'm putting into my body, I am careful and have never overdosed. So there I was, working and earning good money. I was using opiates recreationally, and then I suddenly found I had become addicted, which was a nightmare because you have always got to feed your addiction. Suddenly the work dried up – panic – 'What do I do'? I became very sick and very ill. I started using temazepam and amphetamines because I couldn't afford the money to get the effect I wanted. I injected crushed tablets and got blood poisoning. I lost about three stone and, all of a sudden, the experience of going into hospital and being told I had serious blood poisoning was the crunch. Your sense of immortality comes to a grinding halt. I realised that I was in deep 'shtuck' and had to sort myself out.

"I refused to stay in hospital as an in-patient, so they gave me a double dose of antibiotic – the strongest there was – and told me that if nothing happened within 24 hours and I didn't return, they wouldn't be held responsible. Luckily it did work but before that, I couldn't close my hand. My skin was all yellow, all over my fingers and creeping up my arm, I had great swollen areas of pus. I know that if I had left off hospital attendance for another two days, it would have been curtains. I got my syringe exchanges at the chemist okay, but Mediswabs were very expensive so I didn't use any, which is how I got the poisoning.

"When you are taking 150-200 mls of methadone a day, that is quite a large habit. I always bought my drugs in London in the West End, mainly from private doctors scripts. You buy from people who want to fund their habits, and that is how I got into that scene.

"So, I had no money, what could I do? I am not a thief, so I put that idea out of my head. I looked very emaciated and slightly jaundiced from the effects of drug poisoning. All I got from my own doctor was some Librium which was totally useless, I could have taken the contents of the whole bottle and it wouldn't have done any good at all. My doctor gave me a referral letter to a centre, so he must have realised that I was serious. When I approached them I was told that I would have to wait for two weeks for an appointment. I managed to borrow money off my friends and kept my addiction as low as possible for those two weeks. As soon as I got to the centre, not looking good, sweating and feeling rough, my counsellor told me not to worry, that I would not leave without a script for 70mls per day. It wasn't as much as I was taking, but I was grateful for anything that would put me back to a normal life, which it has done.

"I have now been attending the centre for about eight or nine months and my dosage has been reduced to 40 mls per day. I look much better; I rallied round very quickly and have put the weight back on rapidly.

"I now live at home with my parents who are elderly, and I tend to protect them. Although they did notice when I was at my worst, since attending the centre I have improved so they are quite happy. I still take amphetamines very occasionally but I don't want to cut off the centre support. They know that if you have been a recreational user for such a long time, you can't just turn it off. They don't put rules of prohibition onto people. I am still using drugs sometimes and only recreationally. It was only opiates which finally got me pinned down and ruined my life.

"The drug habit becomes an inner need and you have to keep on taking it every day. I don't think I would ever go back to opiates; it takes over your life. No-one gives the drug to you – you have to go and get it, which is hard work. I used to go up West as soon as I finished work and rake around to get what I needed, it took over my life. You lose a lot of weight just worrying whether you will be able to get more drugs, it gets on your nerves.

"Everyone is entitled to do what they want to do. If people ask me what will happen to them and what they can do to themselves, I'll tell them; but I won't give advice which I know they won't take. If they want to use drugs, they make the decision. You will never find me sitting down and whingeing. I bought the ticket and I took the ride."

'Sandie'

After Sandie was born her father left home, leaving her mother to look after two children on her own. From early childhood, Sandie was taught to be 'strong'. During her teen years, whoever she associated with was considered to be beneath her so Sandie says she became very rebellious and decided to move out.

Unfortunately, as so often happens with children who lose a parent in early life, Sandie had developed a very low opinion of herself. At the age of seventeen she was still very innocent, and became involved with, and moved into a house occupied by, as she called them: "alcoholics, dropouts, drug takers and chaps dossing for the night."

At this time, whoever Sandie became friendly with was in some way connected with either alcohol or drugs. She says: "I was very naive in those days and really didn't know what was what. I certainly didn't realise that everyone was leading everyone astray."

From Sandie's account, it appeared that whoever she took up with was either strongly into alcohol, drugs or was dealing, as well as using, the various substances. Sandie was smart enough to realise that she WAS being conned, when she found herself admitting to the police that she was in possession of LSD – her first criminal offence. The person she was involved with had persuaded her to confess that the substance was hers!

At the age of 19, Sandie was raped. She claims: "I had never been touched by a man before and this made me feel very guilty since I wanted to save myself for the right person – whether this would be with someone with marriage prospects or a long-term relationship – and the actual experience made me feel dirty.

After some time, Sandie developed a relationship with a man who turned out to be a woman-beater. At the beginning he was reasonable, but soon developed violent tendencies He threatened to kill Sandie's mother, her brothers and even her cat; and, after three years of hell, Sandie eventually left him. Her next relationship was with an alcoholic and drug addict who eventually died from drug addiction. At first Sandie resisted the many temptations which came her way but, eventually, after Pip died, she went on a four week alcohol binge. She says now: "I didn't realise how dangerous this could be and finished up in hospital with septicaemia, which nearly cost me my leg. I had developed a temperature of over 106 degrees. This was the result of drinking strong beer and spirits just to give myself some moral support. Instead, after that I became very nervous and withdrawn."

When Sandie left hospital, she says, she really wanted to stop drinking; but, as she recalls: "When you are with about sixteen blokes in a room who are all knocking it back, it is very hard to resist. I needed it to give me dutch courage to carry on. I was living in a house where people were injecting, drinking, using every kind of drug under the sun and dossing down to sleep it off."

Sandie was working part-time by then and had a very nasty boss who, she says, made her life a misery. "I used to walk to and from work and sometimes when I got home, the place would be locked and I would have to wait for one of the drunken louts to let me in."

Sandie's first drug experience was with cannabis. She then progressed to amphetamines, but she did not like these as they made her feel terrible when they began to wear off. After that she tried LSD and recalls: "Most of my friends had marvellous trips but afterwards you feel desperately hungry. LSD made me giggle a lot but it also made me feel physically sick. My other experiments with drugs were cannabis which made me sick; speed, which made me feel physically drained afterwards, and ecstasy, which didn't really come up to my expectations."

Sandy became a health freak and would punish herself by pushing herself to the limit, permitting herself one bottle of cider per week which, she claims was her only escape. "The cider really did me a lot of harm, even though it was only a small amount, because I tortured myself so much over it." At that time, Sandie discovered some magic pills (as she called them) which were reputed to help stop drinking by making the person sick whenever they took alcohol. The woman who supplied them was getting them from a so-called 'bent' doctor. Sandie recalls: "I knew that I needed them to stop me from drinking, so I bought them. After four days of taking what I later found out to be methadone (they should have been Antabuse) I stopped drinking. The tablets gave me terrific energy and I couldn't stop doing things. This wasn't the same effect which I got from speed where I used to feel really drained afterwards. I also took co-proxamol which were given to me by my doctor and I would take between five and ten at a time. It was either that or alcohol; I had to have something to give me mental stability. I never actually tried injecting but saw others do it and it was horrible."

Another way in which Sandie tried to stop her drinking habit was to take valium, though she never mixed these drugs.

It was at this time that Sandie had an accident while crossing the road. She fainted while under the influence of drugs and, because of the massive dosage of co-proxamol over the period of a year,she became frightened and sought help. She was taken into hospital, where she spent four months. Sandie recalls: "Every morning when I woke up, I couldn't believe that I was free from pressure and drugs."

After leaving hospital, Sandie returned to prescribed drugs. But, although her drinking had stopped and she remained dry for about a year, she continued to take co-proxamol. Gradually, the dosage again reached gigantic proportions. She claims that she took between 180 and 190 tablets in the space of a year.

Once Sandie got back into her home environment, she became involved with sexual inter-mixing. She claims to have spent nights with both sexes at once but denies having intercourse.

Sandie reports: "I once tried to kill myself by taking over 90 paracetamol tablets. I finished up in intensive care after having my stomach pumped out. A friend of mine took far less than me and died, but I managed to pull through. After that I began to think about things and decided it was time I sought help. I started attending a drug rehabilitation centre and, together with counselling, I managed to gradually reduce my methadone script, which is now down to 17ml per day."

Sandie had one major relapse when, apart from her usual scripts which she obtained from the centre, she managed to exchange her valium prescriptions for methadone. This increased her intake back up to 70 or 80ml. She says she confessed this to her doctor at the Centre and was told that this quantity by today's standards was quite reasonable! She then started her reduction programme again and, so far has not had another relapse.

During her rehabilitation programme, in order to break the culture that supports drug misusers, Sandie was advised not to visit her friends. She can contact them by letter but, since this is supposed to be the start of a new life, old contacts need to be shed, and she has not been in touch. Her aim is to get into a fully satisfying lifestyle without the aid of drugs. She claims: " You learn by your own mistakes. I am only human and, to me it is a real achievement to leave drugs alone. I want to come off methadone completely; I haven't really liked or respected myself for a very long time.

On a recent visit to her doctor, Sandie was told she would have to have an operation on her feet. "This is not vanity, the doctor said he had never seen such bad bunions on anyone my age before. I am dreading this, because since I take methadone, they are going to look down on me." But of course, they won't. Hospitals are too busy to be judgemental.

Since she joined the programme, Sandie's mother has tried to become much closer to her daughter and visits her frequently. Her advice to anyone contemplating drug use is: "I have never heard anyone who took drugs or drink say that they have not regretted taking either. It might not affect you for years but eventually it certainly will."

'Lindsay'

Lindsay is the second youngest son in a family of nine children. He claims: "I don't come from the traditional family background of a loving Mum and Dad. By the time I came along, it had really worn a bit thin." His father was not a healthy man but he ran a business, paid the household bills and repairs, and that was all. Lindsay continues: "Mum let me do what I wanted to do. I was meant to be at school but often skived – no-one ever checked up and my parents didn't really bother, they were quite happy for me to do my own thing."

Lindsay's involvement with drugs began when he was fifteen years old. He began to mix in with the street culture and joined a group living in a squat who regularly went drinking in a pub. During one of their group get-togethers, a joint was passed round; and, as Lindsay recalls: "There wasn't any big decision about 'should or shouldn't', I just took it and had a couple of puffs."

As he recalls, this was the first experience of drugs out of the way. There was no reaction such as getting stoned or other feelings, it was neither good nor bad. Lindsay felt that it was more important to win acceptance from the group than to take drugs. Smoking was also added, something he did openly at home as well as outside. He recalls: "No-one stopped me, so the bravado bit about smoking making you grown up probably lasted about five minutes. Even when Mum found out I was taking drugs, it really didn't matter. I felt very rejected and, by the time I became officially sixteen, I had already left home. Feelings for my family didn't exist and, out of eight other siblings, I only really liked two."

During Lindsay's teenage years, drugs were only one small part of his daily life; other activities included weekend and holiday fights at the coast, rock and roll party nights, motor cycles and a host of other pastimes which were just as important. Lindsay says: "You have to live and experience this culture. There were those whom we called 'the Plastics' who became anarchists on a Friday night and returned home on Sunday to their nice suburban homes and to Mum and Dad. We, on the other hand, lived in jeans in our dirty squats and our highlight was the pub on a Friday night. The rest of the week we struggled through until the next Friday – it was just survival."

Lindsay was not working but because he came from a family business background, there was always a job there if he wanted one. He said: "I drifted more and more into the culture because it was preferable living with a group that I got on well with and who accepted me rather than with siblings I didn't like or get on with."

Lindsay managed to earn bits of money from doing odd labouring jobs and there was also the dole money. The group survived on very little and there was always someone who would buy a drink or make sure that food was available – it was survival on real basic fundamentals.

The next experimentation with drugs came at the age of sixteen when Lindsay turned to speed. This was obtained from a Hells Angel who sold drugs. Lindsay's ambition was to join the Angels but at that time he was too young – the qualifying age was twenty-one. His reason for buying speed was so that he could meet one of the Angels. Lindsay bought three tablets (blues) for £1. In those days, the drug was in tablet form although nowadays it is more often sold in powder form. He took all three tablets, washed down with a pint of lager. He recalls: "I had no idea what the drug was or what its effect would be and waited for something to happen. I was still waiting when the pub closed. I jumped on my bike and rode off to get a burger after which I visited a pal some distance away at two in the morning. I got back to my place at seven in the morning and told the group what I had taken and that I was still waiting for something to happen. I was told, 'You idiot, this one keeps you awake!' At the time I thought what a complete waste of time it was but then realised that when you have things to do, it was an ideal way to keep awake."

After giving speed a try, Lindsay changed groups and moved into another squat where hard core drugs were more prominent. This took up more time in their daily life when they got 'stoned' during the day and 'partied' during the evening. This was rather like vampire bats, as Lindsay described it – everyone came alive at night! This was also Lindsay's introduction to psychoactive drugs such as magic mushrooms and LSD. As he describes it: "When I took my first trip, that completely blew me away. It is a whole different world compared to the softer types of drugs. Even after my first trip I didn't want to rush back and do it again too quickly. I was happy to leave it for a while. I have never had a bad trip and have always enjoyed my LSD. It is rather like getting a little message at the back of your mind telling you that it is time to take another LSD trip. I can't honestly say that I would never take another one but at this time in my life I don't particularly want to. There are certain drugs which I would never touch again but I can't say that about LSD. The reaction is so different; it was like travelling without going anywhere. Trips lasted for about 6 – 8 hours. Going outside is uncomfortable and does not feel safe since the outside world is so different."

The next drug Lindsay tried was magic mushrooms. He was also smoking a lot of dope, although he still claims that it was not a major part of his life. "I did it often enough to be a drug user, at least three or four times a week but I could still take it or leave it – none of the drugs I was using then were addictive."

The squat Lindsay shared with his group was in a derelict housing estate. No rent was paid but they were charged for electricity and gas. The group socialised with some hippies but did not mix with two recent additions who were junkies, addicted to heroin.

At this time Lindsay was sent to prison for three months, charged with causing criminal damage. On his release, he went to stay with three other pals and it was then that the addictive drug use really started. Prison had no effect on him at all, he says, although he did think briefly about getting himself sorted out; the environment in which he mixed stopped him from making the effort. Drugs such as cannabis, amps, speed and LSD were still part of his lifestyle and there were even a few pills such as temazepam jellies thrown in. The group shared the squat with a 'getaway driver' who used heroin to calm himself down after some of the fast drives, mainly to fool the police. "It was hard to believe that, after one of those injections, you had just driven a getaway lorry at great speed," remembers Lindsay.

Lindsay felt that this was the answer after coming in from a hectic motor bike chase and he looked up some information about heroin which claimed that if one didn't take it every day, it was non-addictive. This was just what he wanted to hear. Lindsay says that, since he was now a big boy, he felt he could handle it and subsequently tried it. He said: "The first time I tried it, it made me really sick. To begin with, it was smoked – I didn't inject for quite a long time, and then the sensation was really amazing. It was not the same as LSD, it was really warm and comfortable, no nervous anxiety. You feel as if your body is a shell and everything inside is hollow. It is not hallucinogenic, and you can increase or decrease the dose as you want. The first thing I found out about heroin was that in cold weather you don't have to switch on electricity since it makes you feel nice and warm and it was certainly easier and cheaper to use 50p's worth on heroin than to put 50p in the meter."

Now Lindsay decided to discard anything which he had previously been using and take heroin exclusively. He compared the effects of drugs on a scale of 1-10 and it showed dope as 2/3, speed as 4/5 and heroin as 8/9... His theory was, why bother with lower scale drugs? so skag became a seven days a week use, rather than just weekends.

This was the start of Lindsay's downfall. He was reasonably 'together' when he began to experiment with drugs but by the time he left his group, he was a complete mess. He recalls: "By the time I moved out, I had moved from recreational use to habitual use. I could take or leave drugs when I moved in but by the time I moved out I had to have them. All my friends in the gang were dropped; you were not allowed to use heroin, and I got thrown out. I became desperate for money; it was no good waiting for Friday night to be with the group, since I had spent the money by Friday morning." The point had been reached when Lindsay had to fund his habit. It was no longer a case of 'if money came along, drugs would be bought'; now there was the need to find money on his own in order to get drugs. By this time, Lindsay was spending about £5 per day.

Those involved in heroin got up in the morning with aching backs, running noses, sweating or chills, and it was obvious that gear was required; but Lindsay could still handle the withdrawal symptoms until evening before he needed to find more drugs. He often experienced blind panic when he couldn't get the money together. He claimed: "At this stage it was more psychological than physical. I'd have all day to get £5 or £10, either by borrowing or making it by getting drugs for others and skimming off enough for myself."

Lindsay continues his story: "The changes in me were horrendous and I didn't like it at all. You spend a lot of time walking, scoring, finding money for the drug and you think a lot while you are walking. I didn't want to be an addict but to stop it involves pain and to stop the pain it involves change. It requires courage to stop which I didn't have, and also not knowing how to do it. You can't just say, 'next week I'm going to stop', you virtually survive by the hour.

"I didn't know any straight people I could stay with. There was nothing other than this scene, no CV to get a job with – 'I am a professional addict', what else is there to say? You meet schoolmates who wouldn't give you the time of day; most of them didn't even recognise me. Once we all had the same chance – they went legit, I went down the drug culture path. You don't like it when you see those kinds of comparisons.

"You can look at it two ways. I can say I really like the culture I'm with. Not many people would experience my kind of lifestyle. Life is about living and I've walked on the wild side – the depraved side. There is no doubt about it, it can be fun.

"The physical side though was really rock bottom. My weight went right down, my waist measurement went from 34" to 28", and that was when it really hit home. My appetite went off to almost nil, except for the odd sweet things. Heroin is an appetite depressant – I was eating something like every other day. By this time I was injecting and spending about £25 per day, and when you are not working, it takes some doing to find that kind of money. I was doing a lot of ducking and diving, surviving on shoplifting, falsifying social security and any other skullduggery, like bits of dealing, just to get by. I had now become a dealer since people knew that if they wanted drugs, I could get it for them. Days melted into weeks, months and years and, although I didn't like my lifestyle, I got used to it and could still see myself being there."

Instead of going for supplies three or four times daily, Lindsay started to buy in bulk; and when that was gone, he would go back for more. To begin with it was mainly dope, but later it became a whole mixture of drugs. He claims: "There is really no distinction between recreational and habitual drugs, it depends largely on the user and how it is used."

There is always the thought at the back of the user's mind that he/she might overdose since the strength of the drug is an unknown quantity. However, little nods are often given, indicating that a particular batch should be watched for possible increased strength. Lindsay claims he was never in the price range to overdose, and besides, he was careful and knew what he was doing.

The police eventually caught up with him coming out of his supplier's house. Fortunately for Lindsay, he had missed the drugs and only had a wad of money to show for it plus a very small amount for personal use. Thus he was alerted that the police were wise to his activities and, as he put it: "I wasn't going to default twice."

Nevertheless, once again Lindsay came before the magistrate – this time charged with an accumulation of past offences like shoplifting, possession of Class A & B drugs and a string of others to be taken into consideration. He recalls: "I kept getting bailed so that all the charges could be taken into consideration at once and I knew that with all that lot against me I wasn't going to get away with it. I was a habitual offender, and was going to do time for it.

"At that time I had a brilliant probation officer who managed to get me into rehab at Phoenix House during the lunch breaks of my court hearings. I was given the choice between prison and Phoenix House and, naturally I chose the latter. The magistrate gave me four weeks trial at rehab but warned me that failure to get sorted out would see me in prison for at least two years.

"I can tell you that prison is child's play compared with rehab – it is really hard work. I completed my four weeks and progressed in leaps and bounds – I really changed. I felt very comfortable there once I had learnt the rules. I liked the peer group I was with since there was no bravado; I had lived for years with people where I had to project an image like 'don't mess with me, there'll be trouble if you do'; I can hold my own, and we often fought like sewer rats.

"Here it was so different since everyone came from the same background and we could just be ourselves. It was like a weight off my shoulders – a real relief. I began to enjoy the culture, the 9-5 work routine – they made us work really hard.

"My heroin addiction was taken completely out of my hands once

I got to the centre. I got no help in the reduction; it was cold turkey all the way. It took about ten days to cross the pain barrier and you walked about with what was like a bad case of 'flu all the time. It was all played down and we were discouraged from moaning and groaning since we were all in the same boat. It took me months to re-establish a natural sleep pattern again and I spent many a night sitting on the top step of the staircase stroking the cat."

Lindsay stayed at the centre for seven months. During his probationary period he quickly progressed and got internal promotions so that when he re-appeared in court, he got glowing reports and references. The programme lasts for twelve months in total, but Lindsay decided after those seven months that he had lost his commitment to the programme – although not to himself. He wanted to get on with his life outside. He had learned to take responsibility, so he discharged himself with the blessing of the centre.

Unable to reach his sister's home on the evening of his discharge, he made his way down to some arches by the river where he and his group used to hang out. It was July and a warm night. Lindsay recalls: "I had flashbacks of my previous life; and then, amazingly, I found some heroin in my pocket which had been there for eight months. I took it and promptly crashed out. When I woke up I felt totally and completely disgusted with myself for letting myself down. After that, I never touched the stuff again. It was the waking up in those surroundings which made me feel that I hadn't progressed at all, and that was the real turning point."

Lindsay went to stay with his sister who insisted that he get himself a job. This turned out to be supervising forty drop-out youths whom no-one would employ.He had no qualifications for this kind of work, apart from his own life experience – somehow, he bluffed his way through. Lindsay loved the work and could relate to these boys. He claims to have learnt as much from them as they learnt from him.

Lindsay then got married and saw a career counsellor who advised him to apply for training in the field which he knew best, the subculture of drugs. He trained at a major London hospital for a year with placement at a street agency. He moved to another hospital in Kent where he continued his training; and then continued at college, where he took a counselling course. During his training he had to visit drug centres, and eventually one of these offered him a permanent position as a drug adviser and counsellor to drug addicts. Lindsay is also now qualified to train trainers, and has himself undergone HIV and Outreach training which allows him to work on the street among drug addicts. He is an official instructor for police officers, has developed drug education packages for Kent schools and is involved with social development projects – an extraordinary transformation.

Lindsay's advice to those who are contemplating using or experimenting with drugs is: "If you need to think about whether you will or won't do it, it will not be for you. We never thought about it, we just did it. Don't use anyone else as a yardstick – you may well be different. If you like being in control of your life, don't go anywhere near drugs!"

Postscript

What does the future hold?

What role has society in general played in creating an environment in which, despite massive and expensive international policing and Draconian legal penalties, we have got ourselves accustomed to drug misuse on such a massive scale?

Blame for the spread of drugs is often attached to environmental factors. Poverty and unemployment – also the criminal culture which may perhaps be considered to be related to these – obviously have a part to play, since the existence of an 'underclass' characterised by economic non-productivity, benefit-dependence and virtually permanent exclusion from the increasing affluence of other sections of society must condition many individuals to seek the kind of temporary escape and relief from hopeless misery that are superficially offered by drugs. Also, poverty of education and lack of exposure to 'middle class' moral restraints, combined with peer group support, create lesser barriers to antisocial behaviour.

However, it must be understood that far from everyone in such an environment becomes a drug user. Indeed, more affluent groups of people are often found to frequent the habit; public schools, where parents typically pay fees of twelve or fifteen thousand pounds a year, are no more immune to teenage experimentation with drugs than any inner-city comprehensive. Morality, too, is not the sole preserve of the middle classes: in many poor but close communities, particularly among immigrant groups, there is a strong moral code, often accompanied by an impressive adherence to religious faith. Drug misuse of all kinds is relatively common among the affluent, white, middle-class young; and, as we have previously discussed, it is the 'recreational' misuse of drugs that, by and large, powers the entire supply industry. Probably the key 'driver' of the drugs revolution is availability and cheapness of supply. Nor is drug misuse a 'new' problem (although the present scale is unprecedented). The availability of cheap gin in the 19th century, together with widespread unemployment, increasing social division and a flight from the land to the new industrial urban areas, combined to create a significant social syndrome of alcohol misuse that has never – except during two World Wars – really gone away. But few societies in history have ever been without some means of getting out of their collective brains. The need for escape is simply part of the way we are.

It is probably helpful, therefore, that we try to divorce drugs altogether from questions of morality, as the relationship between drugs and social dysfunction is a moral minefield. It is possible to point the finger at such trends as increasing materialism, the spiritual void at the heart of our society, abandonment of parental responsibility, the abolition of National Service, falling standards of education, American films or an increasingly sensationalist media – indeed, a hundred and one controversial topics of interest to the 'chattering classes'. It is less certain whether anything much can practically be done about the problem on this abstract level. There is no doubt that society as a whole bears the responsibility for the problems of drug misuse, and hence, for finding some sensible means of minimising the damage.

Certainly, the introduction of much tougher penalties, both for supply and possession of prohibited substances, and a major international drive by governments and law enforcement agencies targeting the producer countries – together with fervent educational programmes in schools – have been accompanied only by a rapid increase in drug misuse of all kinds and have, in some people's view, exacerbated the drug problem by driving it underground and discouraging addicted users from seeking help. On the other hand, societies which have liberalised their drug laws have not seen any real improvement either.

In fact, the society in which we find ourselves as we go into the 21st century is drug orientated to a degree not known before. Potent drugs have become much more widely and readily available. It is therefore understandable that when young people grow up in an environment where drug taking behaviour is apparently 'normal' – where the use of substances such as alcohol and nicotine remains perfectly legal, is even presented in the media as desirable; and where powerful drugs are seen to be widely available on prescription – the routine use of drugs becomes an acceptable form of conduct.

Then, there is the inevitable problem for young people of needing desperately to belong, to conform to the group – usually at school, but also at college and in the workplace. Often, such groups adopt a 'them and us' attitude to other groups, for instance football supporters; and a general air of defiant opposition to authority figures, such as teachers and the police (as most of the anti-drugs education programmes are run by these, it is hardly surprising if they have little or no effect!). Once drugs become the passport to acceptance within the young person's immediate society, a tribal 'token' of initiation into adulthood, they become part of a broader culture that will also dictate the young person's taste in music, sport, clothes, bikes, cars and so on, and the way to eventual dependence will be open. Such attitudes are widely encouraged and exploited by commercial interests, where the 'game' is to ensure that the young person does not realise the extent to which they are being manipulated.

Since drugs are now so widely available, and their social use so readily accepted, the pre-existence of a personality disorder may not be such an important factor in drug misuse as previously thought. Drug users are not criminals or 'weirdos' – they are you and me. Psychologically 'normal' users usually manage to stop the habit when their social circumstances change, when the drug becomes unavailable, or if it fails to produce the desired effect. They are not 'at risk', other than from accidental poisoning or overdose. Those who suffer from poor self-image, feelings of inadequacy or neurosis, who are chronically unwell or who have perhaps been abused psychologically or sexually, may be 'dependent' types for whom drugs are just another prop in the theatre of misery. Resolving the underlying craving for love and acceptance may be a major first step in reducing the dependence on drugs which substitute for those basic needs.

The journey from experimentation to dependence has shortened considerably since the days when psychoactive drugs were used only for medical treatment of particular illnesses, and were totally unfamiliar to the general community. In the past twenty years, however, the creation of 'designer drugs' that were once the preserve of expensively-equipped laboratories has become a worldwide cottage industry, at which anyone with a degree in chemistry can try their hand. The massive increase in air travel, 'open border' trade policies, and the exponential growth of media such as the Internet, have made the exchange of drugs and information about drugs far easier to obtain. Monitoring all this activity is virtually impossible for cash-starved authorities, and given the amounts of money involved, a degree of corruption to 'oil the wheels' is probably inevitable. Consequently, while the penalties for dealing in illegal drugs are severe, the financial rewards are astonishing; presenting almost limitless temptations to those craving well-paid adventure and excitement for very little risk, provided they do not themselves become addicted.

Denial of the problem is not just the preserve of the hopeless addict. As an 'addicted' society, we are increasingly turning to palliatives as a way of resolving unexpressed feelings of powerlessness, and of seeking new modes of being at a time of major transitions. We need to acknowledge openly that there is almost universal acceptance of drugs within our community; that illegal drug misuse is largely driven by the demand from affluent recreational users and not by some criminal underclass; that most of us participate in the drug culture unwittingly through the use and misuse of permitted substances – and that powerful commercial interests are involved, which may be unstoppable. Politicians who persistently call for tougher penalties and interventionist policing, and who refuse to debate the alternatives, are crying in the wind. The problem cannot sensibly be resolved by locking up more individuals who, in any case, will simply pursue their drug-related interests in our increasingly chaotic prisons.

It is this significant change from personal to societal addiction which is setting the scene for future problems of drug misuse on a pandemic scale. Hopefully, it will burn itself out, or else science will come up with new and safer technologies for helping people get 'out of their brains'... For surely, some occasional means of escape from the intolerable burdens and pressures of most people's daily lives is (and always has been) an absolute necessity in any society, and acts as a vital safety valve in preventing still worse problems. In the meantime, all we can do as individuals is to respond to the drugs crisis on an individual level – through individual acts of caring, helping others where possible, by working in the community, and by keeping ourselves properly informed about what is happening on our streets.

Appendix

Useful Telephone Numbers

- ADFAM National
  Waterbridge House, 32-36 Loman Street, London SE1 0EE
  National charity for friends and relatives of drug misusers (including prisoners). Offers free advice, family support packs, publications and training courses for social workers, support group volunteers and professionals. Useful booklet: 'Living with a drug user' by Kathy Robson, price £1.10 inc. p&p.
  Helpline: 0171 928 8900 (10am-5pm, Mon-Fri. 24-hr ans.)

- Central Drugs Prevention Unit (Home Office)
  Horseferry House, Dean Ryle Street, London SW1P 2AW
  12 local prevention teams work with community groups in England. Provides a range of published information, including a newsletter – 'Drugs Prevention News' – project reports, etc.
  Telephone: 0171 217 8631.

- Drugs 'Czar'
  Government drugs policy as set out in the White Paper 'Tackling Drugs Together' is made by a cabinet sub-committee, to which Mr Leslie Hellawell, former Chief Constable of Yorkshire police, the so-called 'drugs czar', was appointed an adviser in 1997. He has no

permanent department. Policy is implemented across a wide range of ministries and agencies, including the Home Office, Customs & Excise, the Department of Health, the Health Education Authority, etc. and co-ordinated from within the Cabinet office.

- Health Education Authority (Drugs Department)
Trevelyan House, 30 Great Peter Street, London SW1P 2HW
Sponsors a range of initiatives, including educating schoolkids on the dangers of drug misuse. January 1998, announced a new Drugs Programme targeting schools, in consultation with Drugs 'czar' Leslie Hellawell. Published two leaflets targeting young people: 'Drugs – the Facts' and 'The Score'.
Telephone: 0171 222 5300
Young people worried about alcohol addiction:
Drinkline Youth: 0345 320202
Giving up smoking? Try...
Quitline: 0800 002200

- 'Healthwise'
People living in the North West can telephone Healthwise, which offers general health information and support and has a dedicated drugs information unit.
Helpline: 0800 838909.
For published information, contact Resource Dept. on: 0151 227 4150 *(Justine Burns).*

- ISDD – Institute for the Study of Drug Dependence
32 Loman Street, London SE1 0EE
Independent charity advising on drugs and drug misuse. Clients include United Nations Drug Control programme and European Monitoring Centre for Drugs and Drug Addiction. World's most extensive library on drug misuse includes research briefings, books and publications for sale, including 'D-mag', a magazine targeted at young people, and 'Juice', a special publication for heroin users on Methadone programmes..
Telephone: 0171 928 1211

- Narcotics Anonymous
  Equivalent of Alcoholics Anonymous. Holds confidential group meetings locally for dependent drug users and reformers.
  Helpline: 0171 730 0009
  Information about meetings: 0171 824 8924

- National Drugs Helpline
  Confidential free advice service.
  Telephone: 0800 776600 (24 hrs.)

- Release
  388 Old Street, London EC1V 9LT
  National charity. Started life in the 1960s as a group of radical lawyers concerned with defending the rights of 'pot' smokers 'busted' by the 'fuzz'... Now a general support and information service. Still helps if you're in trouble with the law.
  Hotline: 0171 603 8654 (24 hrs.)
  Information: 0171 729 9904

- SCODA (Standing Conference on Drug Abuse)
  National membership organisation collects and cross-references information from a wide range of drug support agencies.
  Telephone: 0171 430 2341

- TACADE
  1 Hulme Street, Salford, Manchester M5 4QA
  National charity specialising in health and social education for schools. Publishes a wide range of teaching packs on drug abuse, provides consultancy, goes into schools to train teachers or give classes, attends international conferences, etc.
  Telephone: 0161 745 8925